Leading Lean

The Making Of A Kaizen Event

A real-life chronology
of a three-day event including
detailed guidelines and facilitation tips

Leading Lean

The Making Of
A Kaizen Event

A real-life chronology
of a three-day event including
detailed guidelines and facilitation tips

Jerrold M. Solomon

WCM Associates
Fort Wayne, Indiana
www.wcmfg.com

Leading Lean

By
Jerrold M. Solomon

WCM Associates
P.O. Box 8035
Fort Wayne, IN 46898-8035
260-637-8064
www.wcmfg.com

Disclaimer

Demonstrations and illustrations contained herein provide only a
description of general improvement techniques and methods.
Illustrations and directions may not provide all necessary or relevant
information and the authors suggest that you refer to appropriate
equipment manuals specific to the particular task or contact a
qualified craftsman or professional. By purchasing this book and not
immediately returning it after reviewing this disclaimer, you agree
that the authors may not be held responsible for any omissions or
inaccuracies in any information provided herein.

ISBN # 978-0-9662906-9-1

Front and rear cover design by:
Robert Howard Graphic Design
rhoward@bookgraphics.com

Book and text design by WCM Associates

Printed and bound by:
Thomson-Shore, Inc.
Dexter, MI
(734)426-3939

Library of Congress Catalog Card Number: 2005924511

This is a work of fiction. Names, characters, places,
and incidents are either products of the author's imagination or are
used in a fictional manner. Any resemblance to actual events or
locales or persons, living or dead, is entirely coincidental.

*To my wonderful wife, Sheila,
who has been my inspiration for twenty-six years,
and to my children, Scott, Aimee, and Whitney,
who have made each and every day of my life
a wonderful experience.*

About The Cover
Lessons From Geese

Fact 1: As each goose flaps its wings, it creates an "uplift" for the birds that follow. By flying in a "V" formation, the flock has 71% greater flying range than if each bird flew alone.

Lesson: People who share a common direction and sense of community can get where they are going quicker and easier because they are traveling on the thrust of one another.

Fact 2: When a goose falls out of formation, it suddenly feels the drag and resistance of flying alone. It quickly gets back into formation to take advantage of the lifting power of the bird immediately in front of it.

Lesson: If we have as much sense as geese, we will stay in formation with those who are headed where we want to go and be willing to accept their help and give our help to others.

Fact 3: When the lead bird tires, it rotates back into the formation and another goose flies to the point position.

Lesson : It pays to take turns doing the hard tasks and sharing leadership. As with geese, we are interdependent on each other's skills, capabilities, and unique arrangement of gifts, talents, and resources.

Fact 4: The geese flying in formation honk from behind to encourage those in front to keep up their speed.

Lesson : We need to make sure our honking is encouraging. In groups where there is great encouragement against great odds, the production is much greater. The power of encouragement is the quality of honking we seek.

Fact 5: When a goose gets sick, wounded, or shot down, two geese drop out of formation and follow it down to help and protect it. They stay with it until it dies or is able to fly again. Then, they launch out on their own with another formation or catch up with the flock.

Lesson : If we have as much sense as geese, we too will stand by each other in difficult times as well as when we are strong.

Lessons From Geese, written By Dr. Robert McNeish.

ACKNOWLEDGMENTS

This book would not have been possible without the help and continued encouragement of a number of colleagues. First, I want to thank Larry Rubrich, a World Class Lean practitioner and consultant. Larry has written a number of outstanding books on Lean and I have been very fortunate to have had the benefit of Larry's wisdom. Larry has allowed me to include some of his material in this book. Without his help, this book would not have been possible.

Colin Fox, the Vice President of Manufacturing at Genie Industries, also was instrumental in my ongoing education of Lean principles. Colin has been tirelessly leading the transformation efforts at Genie, a truly World Class company, and always has welcomed my visits to learn as much as I could from his organization. His insights and encouragement are invaluable.

I would like to thank the folks at the Maryland World Class Manufacturing Consortium, (MWCMC), a unique organization funded by the Maryland Department of Business and Economic Development. The MWCMC is a World Class organization in its own right for its groundbreaking efforts assisting Maryland manufacturing companies with their Lean journey. Thanks to the Consortium, especially Bob Barnes and Joyce Sobus, for providing me with continual access to World Class companies and seasoned Lean practitioners.

Special thanks go to my good friend, John Walter, the Director of Lean Manufacturing at MarquipWardUnited. John utilizes all the tools in the Lean tool bag, but more importantly, he understands the critical role of teamwork, communication, and leadership. John continues to be the ongoing source of critical insight who makes the transformation process much easier.

This book, in its format, would never have materialized without the tutelage of Harvey Teres, who teaches English at Syracuse University. I am sure his teaching a manufacturing practitioner the finer points of writing a novel was a much tougher task than his normal assignments of exposing wide-eyed freshman to the literary classics, but he made the task enjoyable and kept me on the straight and narrow.

And of course, special thanks go to my very patient and loving wife Sheila, who, once again, has learned a great deal about another aspect of Lean. She is a constant source of encouragement. Without her assistance, this book would not have been possible.

INTRODUCTION

According to published reports, a large percentage of manufacturing companies are in the midst of Lean or World Class transformations, yet very few companies achieve success. Numerous colleges, hundreds of books, and thousands of web sites provide an unending stream of courses, tools, forms, and the like, to assist with these transformations. I teach such a course at the Business Excellence Consortia which is affiliated with the Milwaukee School of Engineering. Yet, despite all the literature and the growing number of consultants and practitioners ready to assist with the Lean transformation, success is elusive. Why is that?

I believe a successful Lean transformation is eighty percent dependent on people and corporate culture, and only twenty percent dependent on the tools or technical aspects of Lean. By and large, many practitioners have not done a good job explaining that Lean is first and foremost a people system that requires tremendous change in the culture of a company. Whether we are talking about the shop floor, supervision, middle management, or the CEO, the culture must change; otherwise the transformation will never take hold.

Having spent my entire career at North American manufacturing companies, as either the Vice President of Manufacturing or the Chief

Financial Officer, I have been deeply concerned about our ability to compete globally without a radical change in thinking, particularly when it comes to the leadership of people. Like many business people, I learned my lessons from textbooks, articles, training classes, mentors, and on-the-job training. When I finally realized that change was not about numbers and analysis as much as the hearts and minds of our teammates, I turned to the genre that, more than any other, traffics in hearts and minds—the novel. The novel humanizes the problems, illustrates the gut wrenching decisions that have to be made, and provides a perspective not possible in textbooks.

Leading Lean is the second in a series of business novels about the Lean transformation process at Tricor Electronics, a fictional company. It follows the characters originally introduced in *Who's Counting? A Lean Accounting Business Novel*, and exposes the human interactions that occur during any Lean transformation. *Leading Lean* illustrates the angst people go through when asked to change, demonstrates the teamwork and leadership required, exposes the paradigms that must be changed, and lays bare the unwavering commitment required from everyone, especially the CEO. It brings to life the unending stream of interpersonal challenges as the novel chronicles the hour-by-hour progression of a three-day lean continuous improvement event, or as some call it, the kaizen blitz or rapid improvement process. *Leading Lean* demonstrates the critical role a trained facilitator plays in successfully navigating the Lean transformation and provides a road map that will enable your company to compete more effectively in the twenty-first century.

World Class results are achievable on any continent, but only if we unleash the power of the entire workforce by recognizing and encouraging the awesome talent that resides in all of us.

TABLE OF CONTENTS

TRICOR ORGANIZATION CHART

Fred Chapman, *Chief Financial Officer*

Randy Larsen, *Director of Research and Development*

Mike Rogers, *Vice President of Manufacturing*

Christy Kimball, *Director of Information Technology*

Steve Taylor, *Vice President of Sales and Marketing*

Jack Southerton, *Senior Product Manager*

Peter Worthington, *President*

Josh Jenkins, *Senior Design Engineer*

Harold Palm, *Tool Crib Attendant*

Anthony Robinson, *Maintenance Mechanic*

Joe Delaney, *Operator, Work Center 111*

Hubert Powell, *Operator, Work Center 222*

Wendell Givens, *Operator, Work Center 111*

Randall Martin, *Sub Assembly Supervisor*

Paul Carney, *Machine Shop Supervisor*

Barb Bonner, *Human Resources Manager*

Joan Russell, *Master Production Scheduler*

CHAPTER 1
5S EVENT ANNOUNCEMENT

"So, Fred, I hear you're part of the 5S event taking place next week?" asked Randy Larsen, Tricor's Director of Research and Development.

"Yeah. How'd you know, Randy?"

"How could I not know; there are posters all over the place listing the team members. That's quite a roster. I can't believe how much time we're devoting to cleaning a machine. Don't you guys have anything better to do?"

"Hold on, Randy. At least I'm giving this a chance by taking part in an event. That's more than you can say. Talk to me after it's over and I'll let you know what I think. Until then just keep your opinions to yourself. Do you think it was easy getting all those volunteers?"

Randy had a good laugh as his oversized midsection gyrated in rhythm with his husky voice. "Volunteers? You gotta be kidding. I heard you practically had to bribe everyone."

"It's not funny. So maybe it did take some persuasion. The point is we have to get started with these 5S events and we need participation from all over the company. That's the only way it'll work."

"Who says?"

"Mike."

"I gotta hand it to Mike; he's sure convinced you about this Lean stuff."

"He's doing a great job so far, no thanks to you. Hey, I'm late for a meeting so I'll catch you later. In the meantime, please keep your comments about the 5S event to yourself, at least until it's over and we can talk about it. Would you do that?"

"Fred, what are friends for? I'll buy you lunch next week and we can talk about it then."

"That's a deal," said Fred as he turned around and quickly headed back to his office.

Tricor was embarking on its first 5S event in the shop that included folks from accounting, engineering, marketing, and information systems. A number of events had already been conducted in the plant with virtually all plant personnel, and Mike Rogers, the Vice President of Manufacturing for Tricor, decided it was time to break down the walls and get the entire company involved. Mike preferred to include the other departments earlier in the process, but didn't take on that challenge given all the other hurdles he had to overcome in manufacturing. The time was right now that he had convinced Fred Chapman, the Chief Financial Officer, of the merits of Lean. Fred was the ally he needed in the administrative area to make this work.

Fred Chapman loved his job at Tricor Electronics, but everything changed when Mike came aboard. Fred was Tricor's Chief Financial Officer for the past twenty years and spent his entire business career at the company after he completed a five-year stint at a Big 4 accounting firm. He was 60 years old, well respected in the local financial community, and was looking forward to a part-time teaching position at the local business school upon his retirement.

Mike Rogers was the typical hard-charging manufacturing executive who could care less about corporate politics. He was forty-four years old, five feet nine, rail thin, and an avid jogger. He had a job to do and was in a hurry to implement sweeping changes. Mike joined Tricor because he was promised carte blanche to institute the changes necessary for a successful and rapid implementation of Lean.

Fred and Mike got off to a very rough start but worked out their differences. Fred initially resented Mike's intrusion into the financial reporting practices of Tricor and also feared Mike was after his job. After a grueling eighteen months, the two of them worked things out and Fred became a big supporter of Mike's Lean initiatives.

It was Friday afternoon and Fred was organizing the papers on top of his desk into neat piles when the beep from his computer indicated the receipt of another e-mail. Fred swiveled in his chair, cupped his mouse with his right hand and opened the e-mail. It was a reminder from Mike about the three-day 5S event kicking off at 7 A.M. sharp on Monday morning.

Fred read the e-mail and couldn't help but notice the words, "This is a 'hands on' activity. Wear clothes that can get dirty. They will!" What've I gotten myself into, he thought. His phone rang and he reached over to pick it up.

Christy Kimball, the Director of Information Technology, was on the phone. "Fred, did you see the e-mail from Mike yet?"

"Sure did," replied Fred, knowing full well what was coming next.

"How much work does Mike really expect out of us?" asked Christy. "I'll wear jeans, but I'm not climbing all over the machines."

"Settle down, Christy. It won't be that bad. There will be a team of ten of us to get the job done. You'll have plenty of help. Hold on a second, my other line's blinking." Fred put Christy on hold and picked up the other line. It was Steve Taylor, the Vice President of Sales and Marketing.

"Fred, I know Mike spoke to all of us about this 5S event, but Jack just unloaded on me. He isn't too happy about spending three days next week working in the plant on the horizontal boring mill. Can you talk to Mike and see if you can get Jack excused from the event?"

"Steve, let me get right back with you. I'm on the other line with Christy."

"Okay, but make it quick. I have to let Jack know."

Line two went dead and Fred hit the button for line one. "You still there Christy?"

"Yep."

"That was Steve. Evidently Jack isn't too happy about being on the 5S team either, and he complained to Steve."

"Fred, quite honestly, none of us are thrilled about this. I only agreed because you asked me to, but I don't like it. I joined this company to work in IT, not the machine shop. I just don't see why this is so important."

"Christy, I'm just asking you to reserve judgment about this until after the event. Would you at least do that?"

"I'll give it a chance, but I don't know if I'll stay for all three days of the event."

"You'll have to. Now I have to get back to

Steve. See you first thing Monday morning," said Fred, and then he clicked for a new dial tone and dialed Steve's extension.

Jack Southerton was an up and coming star in the marketing department. He was a senior product manager working on a number of key projects for Steve Taylor.

"Thanks for getting back to me, Fred," said Steve, glancing at the digital display to see who was calling.

"What's the problem?" asked Fred tentatively.

"Don't give me that line Fred. You know all too well what the problem is. I can't afford to give Jack up for three days to clean a machine."

"C'mon, you committed to letting Jack be part of the team."

"I know, but now that the event's here, I really can't afford to lose him."

"Just make believe Jack's on vacation. You do let him take vacation occasionally, don't you?"

"Of course, but that's different," bemoaned Steve.

"Listen Steve, we can discuss this all you want, but the bottom line is Peter's made it clear we'll all participate in at least one event this year. Let's see what you think after we get through this event. If it's worthless, we can bring it up with Mike and Peter."

"So, you won't support me in getting Jack excused?"

"I can't, not at the last minute. It's not fair to the rest of the team and that includes me."

"I guess this conversation is a waste of time," said Steve, and he hung up.

Peter Worthington, Tricor's president, had made it clear that every salaried employee would take part in a Lean event during the year. That was music to Mike's ears; he knew it would be the only way to get the participation needed for Lean to succeed at Tricor.

Fred leaned back in his chair and reread the announcement Mike had e-mailed.

Tricor

Lean Enterprise

5S Process Improvement Event

Work Center 111 – Horizontal Boring Mill

March 29th – 31st

Kickoff Meeting: Monday, March 29th at 7:00 A.M.

2nd Floor Training Room

Team Members

Fred Chapman – Chief Financial Officer

Joe Delaney – Operator – Work Center 111

Paul Carney – Machine Shop Supervisor

Wendell Givens – Operator – Work Center 111

Jack Southerton – Senior Product Manager

Christy Kimball – Director of Information Technology

Anthony Robinson – Maintenance Mechanic

Josh Jenkins – Senior Design Engineer

Hubert Powell – Operator – Work Center 222

Randall Martin – Sub Assembly Supervisor

Harold Palm – Tool Crib Attendant

Facilitator – Mike Rogers – VP Manufacturing

Please note the following:

1. Attendance for the entire workshop is absolutely critical. If you cannot commit to the entire event, please notify Mike Rogers immediately.

2. The workshop will be held from 7:00 AM to 3:30 PM Monday through Wednesday. It may be necessary to work overtime on Monday or Tuesday and that will be decided by a team vote if necessary.

3. This is a "hands on" activity. Wear clothes that can get dirty. They will!

4. Lunch will be provided each day.

See you all Monday morning!

Mike

CHAPTER 2
WE'VE ONLY JUST BEGUN

DAY 1 (6:30 A.M.)

Mike paced in front of the training room going through a mental list of the topics he would be covering. He was a bundle of nerves before each Lean event despite the fact that he had done this hundreds of times. He had three days to bring ten to twelve individuals, each with a different agenda and personality, into a cohesive team. The only thing they all had in common was they didn't want to spend the next three days with him.

"Good morning Mike," said Fred as he walked over to the back of the room and set down two boxes of donuts and a container of coffee on a table against the back wall.

"Good morning," responded Mike from across the room. "Get a load of you. Never thought I'd see you in jeans. Didn't think you owned a pair."

"Yeah, right. Brooks Brothers has a special

department for CFOs who need jeans for their 5S events. It's one of their fastest growing departments. I picked up the jeans Saturday and there was quite a crowd in there all looking forward to their Monday morning 5S's."

"I bet. Thanks for bringing the donuts. I really appreciate it!"

Fred opened one of the boxes and helped himself to a jelly donut. "I've just as much riding on this event as you do."

"What do you mean?" Mike asked quizzically as he walked to the back of the room to help Fred set up the condiments.

"Do you really think it was easy getting someone from engineering, marketing, and IT to attend this event?"

"Was it that bad, Fred?" asked Mike, slightly taken aback.

"You bet it was. I expended a lot of my political capital getting Randy and Steve to free up someone from their area for three days. It was like pulling teeth."

Randy Larsen, Tricor's Director of Research and Development, was always up against seemingly impossible deadlines and it took Fred three lunches to finally convince him to let Josh Jenkins attend the event.

"How about Christy? Was she a problem

also?" asked Mike.

"She wasn't too happy, but since I'm her boss, it was a lot easier," responded Fred as he headed over to take a seat at one of the tables.

Mike followed behind Fred and continued to the front of the room where he had a small table with his class materials stacked in color coded files for easy recognition. He slumped into the chair and took a deep breath. "That's really disappointing. With all the activities Christy's been involved with already, I assumed she'd be a little more excited to see what this is all about."

"C'mon Mike, get real. Don't forget that all those other changes were in her comfort zone: new programs, use of the internet, and stuff like that. She liked the challenges and the learnings. She really can't see that happening in a 5S event."

"She'll learn a lot from this as well; you just wait and see. . ."

"Good morning," said Josh as he entered the room and made a beeline for the back table. "Ah, donuts and coffee, just what I need."

"Good morning, Josh. Ready for the event?" asked Mike as he hustled to the back of the room to shake Josh's hand.

"Do I have a choice?"

Mike let the comment pass. The rest of the

participants filed in, one by one, got their coffee, and took seats at the tables. Mike went around the room, introduced himself when necessary, shook each person's hand and made a point of thanking them for coming to the class. For the most part, they silently acknowledged his comment. They engaged in small talk while waiting for Mike to finish his rounds and begin the meeting. They didn't look like the happiest bunch in the world and Mike knew he'd have his hands full. On the flip side, if all went well, they would be the best ambassadors of Lean that he could hope for.

It was a little past seven when Mike returned to the front of the room and began the event by welcoming everyone. Then he asked everyone to do three things: first, introduce themselves; next, explain what, if any, exposure they had to Lean; and finally, provide a couple of objectives they personally had for this event.

Mike turned to Christy who was seated at the front left of the horseshoe arrangement of tables. Christy had short cropped hair and was always well dressed. She had an air of confidence about her that broadcast to all that she knew her stuff. But this appeared to be a different person, one dressed in tattered jeans, a grubby shirt, and very little makeup. "Christy, I see you're dressed for the event. How about starting the introductions for us?"

"Sure. I'm Christy Kimball, Director of Information Technology. I've been with the company for about eight years. I haven't been involved in any Lean events but I've been knee deep in changing a lot of our programs to support the changes we're making in purchasing. I want to learn more about what goes on with Lean in the shop and how it might affect my area."

"Josh," said Mike prompting him to start his introduction.

"I'm Josh Jenkins. I'm a Senior Design Engineer and have been at Tricor for about five years. I don't know much about Lean and I'm not sure why I'm even here. I was basically told to attend by my boss, Randy Larsen."

"Josh, we'll be going over some basic Lean principles to get everyone up to speed on what this is all about," said Mike.

"It would've helped if I knew a little more about what I was getting into before this event started," responded Josh.

"Didn't Randy explain any of this to you?" asked Mike trying to hold back his frustration.

"Not really. He just told me to be here for the next three days. He didn't seem very happy about it either."

"That's what happened with me also," said Jack Southerton, who was sitting next to Josh.

Mike did all he could to control his anger. "That's not a problem, Jack. We'll spend the first couple of hours reviewing everything and you'll be able to share it with the marketing department. Jack, go ahead with your introduction."

"Okay. I'm Jack Southerton and I'm a Senior Product Manager in the marketing department. I'm here to learn about Lean, I guess."

The introductions continued for the next ten minutes. All of the attendees from the manufacturing departments were somewhat familiar with Lean from Mike's monthly plant meetings, and a few of them had already participated in a 5S event.

After the introductions were complete, Harold Palm, the Tool Crib Attendant, raised his hand. And what a hand that was, thought Mike. Those are the largest hands I've ever seen, probably from working with tools all his life. Harold was about six feet two, two hundred and forty pounds. He had worked at Tricor for more than twenty years and was a very inquisitive person, a pleasure to talk to.

"What can I do for you, Harold?" asked Mike.

"I was just wondering how you decided who should be on this team?"

"Great question," responded Mike as he flipped through a number of PowerPoint slides and finally stopped at a slide entitled:

Mike's Rules for 5S Team Selection

1. Teams will comprise 8–12 members from a cross section of departments.

2. The operators from the work center being 5S'd must be on the 5S team.

3. At least one operator from the next work center to be 5S'd will be on the team.

4. The team will consist of approximately 50% salaried team members.

5. Where appropriate, the maintenance department will be represented on the team.

"Why does maintenance have to be on the team?" asked Anthony Robinson, the Maintenance Mechanic.

"Thanks for asking," said Mike. "Would anyone like to answer that?"

Joe Delaney, the operator of Work Center 111 responded. "I was on a 5S team last month and we had a lot of work for maintenance. Don't know what we would've done without them."

"You got it, Joe," said Mike approvingly. "A really good 5S will typically involve maintenance personnel because air lines, electrical service, equipment, or something will need to be moved or modified. By participating on the team, maintenance understands why it needs to happen and can get right to it."

"So I'll be pretty busy, I guess?" asked Anthony.

"You betcha," responded Mike.

"How about salaried personnel? Why are they on the team?" asked Fred.

"There are a few reasons," said Mike as he walked over to the flip chart in the front corner of the room. He picked up the marker and began to write down a short list.

Salaried Personnel on Lean Teams

1. Financial reasons

2. It's not just for direct labor

3. It's not just for the shop

4. Manufacturing will help in the office

"Let me explain each of these. First, people get antsy when ten hourly employees are devoted to a three-day event. That equates to about 240 hours, or about $3,600 for a 5S event. Initially everyone thinks I'm out of my mind to spend that kind of money cleaning a work area, which is all anyone thinks we're doing. . ."

"Well, isn't it?" called out Hubert Powell, the

operator for Work Center 222, the next area to be 5S'd.

"Hubert, I'll let you answer that when we're all done. Remind me at the report-out session."

"At the what?" asked Hubert.

"At the meeting we'll have when this is all over; it's called the report-out session," answered Mike.

"I sure will," said Hubert confused by what Mike meant but content to let it pass.

Mike continued with his explanation. "So to avoid having everyone worry so much about how much we spend, I try to have five salaried people on each event. That really confuses everyone when they try to figure out what it costs."

"Yeah, but it still costs whether we're salaried or hourly," shot back Christy.

"You know that and I know that, but the financial statements don't know that," responded Mike.

"Now what are you talking about?" asked Fred.

"If we had all hourly people, every traditional manufacturing measure would be depressed, be it productivity, efficiency, or utilization. Isn't that right Fred?"

"That's true," said Fred still puzzled by where Mike was going with this.

"And if we had a lot of people from the same department in the plant, it would really be noticeable, wouldn't it?"

"Of course," said Fred. "So you're saying you hide the expense by using salaried folks?"

"Yes and no," said Mike. "Whether we use hourly folks or not, it still costs the company. It's just that no one ever realizes how much hourly folks can contribute to continuous improvement. Hourly folks are supposed to be producing parts. It's as if they're supposed to check their brains at the door. We can't be a great company until we utilize all of everyone's capabilities. We have to use the experts to fix the processes and the operators are the experts!"

"Right on!" chimed in Wendell Givens, Work Center 111 operator. "Sometimes I can't believe some of the new parts we get. They're almost impossible to make, especially with the equipment we have. I wish they'd just ask me about it first."

"And that's the point, Wendell," said Mike pacing in front of the room hoping Josh didn't take offense to Wendell's comment. It was too early in the event for sparks to start flying. "We need to get you involved if we're ever going to get better. I just don't want to raise a red flag and advertise to everyone how much we're spending on these events until everyone understands what the benefits will be. Once they understand the benefits, they won't care who's on the team."

"When does that happen?" asked Christy.

"Individually, you'll appreciate a 5S event once you've been involved in one. But for the most part, the significant tangible improvements won't occur until you follow up the 5S event with other continuous improvement events such as set-up reductions or kaizens. The point is that you'll never get to those if you don't do a 5S first."

"So 5S's by themselves don't accomplish anything?" continued Christy, trying to box Mike into a corner.

"It depends," responded Mike calmly as he walked over to the chair, rested his arm on the back, and leaned forward. "I've seen set-ups decrease by fifty percent as a result of a 5S in cases where the work place was a mess. I've also experienced significant time savings in material handling just by better organization. We did a 5S in the shop where we wound up returning thousands of dollars worth of material when we right sized the inventory locations and made it impossible for the vendor to drop off too much inventory. In another event, we found over five thousand dollars of tooling stashed away where no one knew about it because the operator no longer worked at the company."

"That seems pretty stupid! Why would anyone do that?" asked Jack.

Mike turned toward Joe with a big grin. "Care to answer that Joe?"

"Sure. Sometimes it's a real pain in the butt to walk back and forth to the tool crib to get supplies so we just keep some extra at our work-stations. Then if we don't need them, we just put them in the drawer, just in case, even though we're supposed to return them."

"Why wouldn't you need them?" asked Christy, genuinely interested in understanding the process.

"That happens a lot because the schedule changes or the job is cancelled altogether," responded Joe.

"Hold on Mike," said Fred, "How about my question? Didn't you say you're trying to hide how much we spend on these events?"

Mike knew he had to get back to Fred's question, but rather than cut anyone off he welcomed the team's participation in the discussion, even if it was somewhat off the main subject. He wanted them to feel comfortable speaking up and sharing their comments and concerns, and ultimately, their ideas.

"Thanks for getting us back on track, Fred. Yeah, I'm sort of trying to hide how much we spend. I don't want to charge the time of ten hourly people to the event as it'll create an eyesore on the results. But think about this, Fred. You know I told all the salaried folks they better plan on working very long days during an event. We'll be at it from seven in the morning to about three-thirty in the afternoon. What'll you do as soon as three-thirty comes?"

Fred didn't hesitate. "I'll go back to my office for a few hours and catch up on all my e-mails and phone messages."

"So will I," said Jack. "I'll probably be here until seven or eight o'clock. I can't ignore my work just because I'm on a 5S event."

"Me too," said Christy.

Mike nodded approvingly. "And so will I. That's the point. During the events, salaried folks have to juggle both jobs. It's a hell of a lot of work but that's the only way we'll improve the company without getting too far behind on the day to day. So in effect, the salaried folks are learning about a valuable Lean tool, learning about the manufacturing process, helping us from pulling too many people out of the production process all at once and possibly jeopardizing the schedule, and allowing us to soften the financial impact of an event. That's why we need everybody pitching in on the 5S's. There are additional benefits but you'll find out about those during the next three days."

Randall Martin, the Sub Assembly area supervisor, raised his hand.

"Go ahead, Randall," said Mike.

"Mike, why you sayin' it's not just for direct labor?"

"Because we want the entire workforce to participate."

"Why?" continued Randall.

"To get the best solution for the challenges we'll face, we need everyone's input. I'm talking about the people that make the product, the people that design it, market it, and so forth. Lean isn't just about what happens in the plant, it's about improving the entire business. And the sooner we get everyone working together and understanding what each of you goes through to satisfy the customer, the better off we'll be. That's why I said it's not just for the shop."

"How about the last item on your list; are we really going to be doing this in the office?" asked Jack.

"Why not?" countered Harold Palm. "I've been in the IT area and there's stuff all over the place. And I once went to accounting to find a report and the place was buried in computer printouts. It took forever to find it...."

Mike interrupted, "Soon we'll have teams work in the office as well. The office folks have exactly the same challenges we have in the plant: looking for stuff, set ups, batch processing, etc. You name it, they have it—it's just harder to see. We've been at this long enough now and we need to get on with the class. I hope now you understand why you were selected."

"Mike, just one more question, please?" asked Josh.

"Okay, go ahead," said Mike, looking at his watch and realizing he was already behind schedule. It was almost twenty to eight and Mike hoped to finish the classroom training portion of the event by nine o'clock. At this pace, he knew he would never make it.

Josh continued, "Why haven't we had any classes on this until now? If we had, then I wouldn't be in the dark about all of this."

"There are two approaches to education," responded Mike. "You can have classes for everyone in the company and spend quite a bit of time before you get to implement anything. I've seen companies spend years studying and educating everyone. Then when it comes time to finally doing something, they've forgotten everything."

"So what's the other approach?" asked Jack impatiently.

"We do what I call just-in-time education. That's what I'm trying to get to now. Lean's about doing, so we have a couple of hours of class followed by two-and-a-half days of learning by doing."

"But don't some people feel left out of the process that way because they don't know what's going on?" asked Hubert.

"That's a good point," conceded Mike. "But with either approach there are problems. I just prefer learning and doing so we can start to realize the benefits that much sooner. Through newsletters and posters I'll try to keep everyone else informed of what's going on. Besides, we talk about Lean at every monthly meeting and I provided a general overview for the entire plant before we started any of this, so this shouldn't be that new to you. Okay now, we really have to get going."

CHAPTER 3
LEAN BASICS

DAY 1 (7:45 A.M.)

Mike went through a few slides to explain the basics of Lean and the paradigm changes required for success. He then went into the core of the class material: the explanation of muda, the types of waste, and, of course, the 5S process. His first slide was on muda.

What is Muda?

◆ Muda is a Japanese word for waste

◆ Muda is anything other than the minimum amount of:

- People
- Time
- Equipment
- Material, Parts, and Space to ADD VALUE to the product.

◆ Muda is all around us every day!

"The key is to begin to see the waste that's all around us every day. About fifty to seventy-five percent of what all of us do each day is unnecessary for one reason or another, but it's invisible. Let me explain what I mean."

"Boy, that would sure help because I've no idea what you're talking about," said Josh, shaking his head.

"This slide will help."

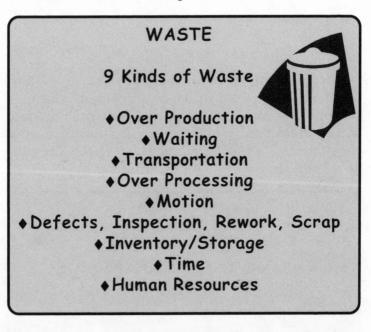

Mike explained each of the categories with examples. There was much discussion and the usual push back from the class, but that was all par for the course. Mike knew it would take a considerable amount of time before everyone began to accept the notion that almost every activity could be done in half the time if everyone worked in teams to eliminate the non-value-added activity.

Hubert was frustrated by the discussion. "Mike, you know we bust our butts in the machine shop and our productivity is higher than ever. You always mention that at the plant meetings. Are you talking about the assembly area?"

"No, I'm talking about the whole company including the machine shop, accounting, engineering, and every other department. We all can do a lot better but we're just not familiar with spotting the waste that's around us all the time, so we don't think anything is wrong."

"Come on, this is so much BS. I haven't heard anything about my area, the tool crib. How about an example of waste there?" asked Harold, obviously proud of what he does and convinced his area was muda free. Harold's challenge grabbed the attention of the rest of the team and they hoped someone finally stumped Mike.

"Okay, Harold, I'll give you two things to think about. First, do you have any idea how much time the machinists spend getting their tools from the tool crib?"

"No, never thought about it that way."

"Try four thousand hours a year."

"You're kidding."

"Nope, think about it. Next, do you have any idea how many dollars you have invested, or I'd rather say, wasting away in tool inventory?"

"It's not a waste," shot back Harold. "We can't afford to run out of anything."

"Let me give you the facts. We have over one hundred and fifty thousand dollars in cutting tools and supplies and we only use about thirty thousand dollars per month. That's five months worth and our distributor can get anything for us in two weeks max and eighty percent of it over night. So why do we need to have so much?"

"We've always had that much. I'm not doing anything differently," responded Harold defensively.

"I know. It's not your fault, it's our fault. My good buddy Fred doesn't even have any idea how much cash is tied up in the tool crib because it's not on our inventory records."

"You're right. So how do you know?" asked Fred.

"Because I went out and counted it. The point is, there's waste everywhere, even in the tool crib, Harold. And it's not just Harold's area, it's everywhere. And if you don't believe me, I challenge everyone in this room to go back to their departments and do the following experiment. Count the first ten or twenty people you see and make a mental note of how many are doing non-value-added work. . . "

"And explain what's non-value-added work again, please," asked Christy.

Mike responded. "Sure, this slide says it all.

Lean Goal - Eliminate Waste

Anything the customer would not be happy to pay for if you listed it separately on the invoice.

So if you were the customer, Christy, and I handed you an invoice that listed every single thing we did to build the product, like moving all the parts around the plant forever and a day, all the rework we did, the time for all the set-ups, the waiting for all the paperwork, etc., with the associated cost for every item, would you gladly pay the bill, no questions asked?"

"Hell no," blurted Christy in her high pitched voice.

"Neither would I, but we can't see all the waste because it's buried in the total cost of the product. So here's what I suggest. Paul, when you walk around the machine shop, make a mental note of how many people are actually changing the form, fit, or function of the parts versus everything else they might be doing. Do this about ten times for perhaps the first twenty people you see and it'll give you a good idea of the percentage of waste in the machine shop. Randall, try the same thing in sub assembly. Jack, Josh, and the rest of you, try it in the office as well. You'll all be shocked."

"So you're sayin' we're doggin' it out there," protested Randall.

"No, no, no. It's management's fault. They're the ones who developed the processes that cause all the waste. We need your help to fix it."

"Can't argue with you about that," said Randall, nodding in agreement for the first time.

Mike flipped to the next slide. "Let's go over exactly what 5S is.

Step #	Japanese Word	English Translation	5S Word
1	Seiri	Proper Arrangement	Sort
2	Seiton	Orderliness	Straighten
3	Seiso	Cleanliness	Sweep
4	Seiketsu	Cleaned Up	Schedule
5	Shitsuke	Discipline	Sustain

"The 5S's originated in Japan, based on an organization and housekeeping system that contained five words all beginning with the letter S. We adopted the process and changed the words to suit our needs. Some companies call it the 5C's while others have added a sixth S for safety and still others have added a seventh S for spirit."

"Didn't the Japanese believe in safety?" asked Joe.

"Of course they did," responded Mike. "Safety was part of the original Japanese 5S process and embedded in every step of the way. They didn't feel it needed to be a separate item."

Mike proceeded to the next slide.

The 5S's are the keys to workplace organization and housekeeping and lead to:

√ An Increase in Quality;

√ An Increase in Productivity;

√ A Cleaner Workplace, which creates a Safer Workplace;

√ A Reduction in Required Space; and,

√ A much easier way to detect equipment malfunctions.

"That sounds like a lot of bull to me," said Randall. Randall was a long term employee who would be content doing the same thing for the rest of his life. He was an excellent worker but he marched to a different drumbeat. He was a loner, wanted to do things his way, and despised meetings. "You mean we're goin' to spend three days cleanin' the place. I don't see how that's gonna help at all."

Mike heard this a thousand times and was just waiting to see who the hardhead in this group was. It never failed. Every group had a problem case and that person usually voiced displeasure with the process before the initial education session was over. Sometimes it was a mild objection, sometimes the person would just tune out the class, and other times it was outright anger at the new ideas. But at least Randall was questioning things. Mike knew he was going to be the thorn in his side for the next three days. All the more pleasure when he finally comes around, thought Mike.

"Randall, 5S is not just about cleaning the place. . ."

"That's what it looks like to me," interrupted Randall.

Mike controlled himself as he knew this would continue for the rest of the event. He had to win Randall over, not alienate him. "Randall, you haven't seen what we've done in the machine shop yet because you work at the other end of the building in sub assembly. We'll be touring some areas that've already been 5S'd later this morning and I'm sure you'll see a difference."

"Makes no difference to me what they do in the machine shop. I like my work space just the way it is. Ain't no one tellin' me what to do."

Everyone was staring at Mike, waiting to see what he would do.

"No one's asking you to change your workspace. We're just asking for your help with Work Center 111 so you'll see what this is all about. After we're done you can decide if it would benefit you in any way."

"Don't need three days sittin' here to know that."

"You won't be sitting here for three days. We'll be in the shop most of the time."

"Makes no difference to me. If that's what I gotta do, then I'll do it."

"Thanks. It's about eight thirty now. Why don't we take a fifteen minute break and meet back here at a quarter to nine."

CHAPTER 4
MORNING BREAK

DAY 1 (8:30 A.M.)

Everybody got up and left the room except Fred. He headed right over to Mike.

"That got a little tense. Does that usually happen?"

"I can't believe you're asking that. When I started here you weren't much different from Randall and for the same reason, I was invading your space—the accounting area."

"C'mon, that was a long time ago, and I was never that bad."

Mike laughed, "You gotta be kidding."

"Are you ever going to let me forget it? Didn't I help get Josh and Jack to attend? Haven't I been supporting you this past year?"

"You've been great and I really appreciate

it, but my point is that Lean intrudes into everyone's space and most people just won't put up with it. They're too comfortable, they hate change. It doesn't matter whether you're in the machine shop, sub assembly, accounting, or wherever, you'll all act the same. It's just a little more shocking when you see someone else do it."

"Boy, you're not kidding. I can't believe I was like that."

"He'll come around. It'll just take a little longer for him. I gotta go get some coffee. It's going to be a long day."

During the break, Josh and Jack sat together in the cafeteria, drinking their coffee and discussing the event.

"So how are we going to make it through these next three days?" asked Josh.

"Man, I just don't know. I've got so much work to do; I can't be sitting here cleaning the place when I'm already up against so many deadlines."

"You have deadlines?" exclaimed Josh. "I have a design review in a month and I'll never make it."

"So how come Randy picked you for the event?" asked Jack.

"It really didn't matter who he picked; we're

all under the gun. I guess I just got the short straw."

"Yeah, Steve wasn't happy about letting me go either, but he said Peter insisted that all the departments participate in these events. He's gotta keep the big boss happy."

Three years ago, Tricor's Board of Directors recruited Peter Worthington after he successfully led two other firms to leadership positions in their industries. Peter's background was impeccable: he was the star athlete at Harvard and one of the most publicized sales executives in the telecommunications and electronics distribution business. With his six feet four well-trimmed frame, perpetual tan, charismatic personality, and exemplary performance record, Peter was exactly the type of executive the Board targeted to increase sales and earnings. And he was betting heavily on Mike's Lean journey to help restore Tricor's competitive position by dramatically improving operational performance.

"We better head back now," said Jack as he glanced at his watch, picked up his coffee, and headed back to the training room. Josh reluctantly followed behind him.

CHAPTER 5
THE DETAILS

DAY 1 (8:45 A.M.)

When everyone was seated, Mike resumed his presentation. "Now I'd like to review each of the 5S's so you all have a good understanding of what we'll be doing for the next three days." Mike put up the next slide.

1st S - SORT

◆ Sort from the workplace what is needed from what is not needed

◆ Add what is needed but not there

◆ General Criteria—if it wasn't used in the last 30 days, or it will not be used in the next 30 days, store it away from the work site.

◆ Use the Red Tag System to identify unneeded items

"The first 'S' is *Sort*." Mike went on to explain how work areas, usually without exception, accumulated parts, supplies, tools, and anything else you could think of, over the course of many years, if not decades, and it was time to sort and remove anything that didn't belong there. As he was explaining this, the machine operators were getting very uncomfortable.

Hubert was first to voice his displeasure. "Why do we need to remove stuff if we'll only need it later? That sounds like waste to me." Everyone else in the room nodded approvingly at what seemed like a very rational question.

It was obvious Mike had heard this question hundreds of times. "Hubert, when we go to the work center and Red Tag the items that are not being used, you'll see how much junk we really have. This extra stuff only gets in the way of finding what you really need, potentially causes safety and quality issues, takes up space that we can put to better use, increases set-up times, and may be needed by other work centers that don't know where to find it."

"I don't think you'll find too much," responded Hubert.

"If it's anything like the other 5S's we've done, you'll be surprised," responded Mike.

"I was on one event and it was scary how much junk we had," added Fred.

"Yeah, right Fred," said Hubert, glancing at

Fred as if to say what the hell does a bean counter know about anything in the machine shop?

"What do you mean by a Red Tag area?" asked Randall.

I'm glad he's at least showing some interest, thought Mike. "That's an area we'll mark off and put all the Red Tag items in."

Paul Carney, the Machine Shop Supervisor, helped Mike out. "I've roped off an area not too far from Work Center 111 that'll be our Red Tag area. It's about twenty feet by twenty feet and should be enough space."

Paul had been a supervisor at Tricor for over twenty years. He was about six feet two, rangy, and always on the move. He seemed to spend the majority of his work day chasing parts, and he felt he didn't have time for these 5S events. This was his second 5S event, but that was all he thought it was, a one-time event. Mike was frustrated that Paul had not yet embraced Lean and he was hoping that continued exposure would help Paul understand the true value of 5S.

"Thanks for letting us know, Paul," responded Mike.

"What about set-up times? Did the last 5S reduce them?" asked Christy.

This was a sore point with Mike. He had

asked Paul to start timing set-ups of key work centers, but Paul didn't have the information ready for the last 5S event. Not having baseline data violated all of Mike's rules and made it impossible to determine the improvements as a result of a 5S event. "We don't have the data from the last event, but we did collect it for this work center," responded Mike confidently as he glanced toward Paul.

"Yeah, I have all that information," added Paul right on cue. "Do you want me to go over it now?"

"No, we'll cover that in the *Just the Facts* section later this morning. Thanks for collecting the information."

"Mike, you mentioned that 5S can improve quality, but how can it?" asked Josh.

"Good question. If we have a bunch of tooling and fixtures at the worksite that aren't needed but are readily available, there's a much greater probability that the wrong item will be picked up and used to create a defective part. We want to eliminate the possibility of that happening. Doesn't that make sense?"

"Sounds reasonable," responded Josh, nodding in agreement.

Mike continued, "Before we move on to the next 'S', I want to explain some rules. The Red Tag area is not our in-house landfill. At the end of the event, the supervisor of the area—in this case that's you, Paul—will have 60 days to disposition everything in the Red Tag area. The Red Tag system is for one-time use only; it's not an on-going crutch for future clean-ups. Make sure all inventory, equipment, tools, fixtures, and jigs are clearly labeled and stored in the appropriate place if they'll be used in the future. We'll develop visual arrangement storage areas which clearly indicate what is being stored, how many there are, and where they might be used. All other items will be thrown away.

Mike proceeded to the next slide.

2nd S - Straighten

♦ A place for everything, and everything in its place

♦ Mark and label everything so that it can be easily found and put away

♦ Store everything close to the worksite

♦ Organize and standardize methods

♦ Use visual arrangement storage techniques

"The next 'S' is *Straighten*. Our goal in the 'Straighten' process is to create a work center where every item that needs to be there has a defined place, and everything is in its place."

"You gotta be kiddin'," said Randall. "I know

exactly what I have and don't need no one tellin' me where to put it."

Mike took a deep breath and responded slowly. "Randall, you probably know where every tool is in your work area, but it probably still takes extra time to actually find it. Also, what happens when you're on vacation or out sick? How can anyone else working in the area possibly be efficient? And what if you accidentally misplace a tool somewhere else in the plant; how will anyone know whose tool it is and where to return it?"

"I don't want anyone else messin' around with my tools—that's why I lock them up in my tool chest every night. Don't see how this will help me."

Mike knew, sooner or later, that in every event the issue of tool chests would raise its ugly head. Now was not the time to break the news to Randall that his tool chest would eventually be eliminated. It wasn't worth the angst so early in this event.

Fred sensed the tension building and helped Mike out by moving to another subject. "What do you mean by visual arrangement storage?"

"It'll be easier to understand if I show you a few slides demonstrating these techniques," responded Mike. He then went through about ten pictures of work areas where all the tools were labeled and hanging on shadow boards or placed inside pre-cut slots in foam boards. When using shadow boards, the outline of the tool is marked so that if the tool is missing, or in use, it is instantly noticeable. If the tool is put away in the wrong place, it is also obvious. The foam boards are a notch above shadow boards as they also serve as error-proofing devices. If the tool doesn't belong in the area, it won't have a space cut into the foam board and therefore won't fit. If drawers have to be used, the foam inserts are inserted into the drawers which eliminates the possibility of extra "stuff" building up. There won't be any room for anything other than what is supposed to be in the drawers. There was even one slide illustrating how far folks went with this as the area around a trash can was outlined and labeled "Trash Can".

"You're not suggesting we label our trash can areas, are you?" said Christy laughing.

"Absolutely," said Mike emphatically. "If it can move, it will, and that causes us to waste time. Harold, why don't you tell everyone what we did with the pallet jacks?"

"Sure," said Harold putting down his donut, wiping his mustache, and standing up as if getting ready to give a speech. "We use eight pallet jacks in the plant. One day, I mentioned to Mike that it seems as if everyone is always walking around looking for a pallet jack to move skids of material, and it's like an Easter egg hunt trying to find them. Mike asked me to get a few people together to figure out a solution to the problem. We worked with all the departments and came up with permanent locations for the pallet jacks when they weren't being used, sort of like their permanent parking garages. After trying a few areas, we settled on what worked best; then, we painted lines, and labeled the floor and the corresponding pallet jack, and have been doing that ever since."

"Did it work?" asked Christy

"Sure did! At first everyone thought it was a joke, but it didn't take long before everyone began using it. And if you ask anyone, they'll tell you it saves time, and lots of it. I don't know why we didn't think of that before."

"That's par for the course, Harold. You didn't think of it before because everyone accepts the fact that that's the way we've always done it. We all have to learn that improving the process is everyone's job. And whether it's pallet jacks or trash cans, it all adds up to a much safer and more competitive business." Okay, enough preaching, thought Mike. "Any more questions on the second 'S'?"

"Just one," asked Josh. "It looks like one of the work benches had the shelves taken out. What's going on with that?"

"During that event, the team determined they didn't need the extra storage areas in the workbench, so they boarded them up."

"Looks like they're just ruinin' a good piece of equipment," complained Randall.

"If it's not needed, it just gets in the way," said Mike. "Horizontal surfaces are magnets for junk. I've seen folks weld drawers shut, replace horizontal surfaces with sloped surfaces, or stuff the area with foam so it can't be used. Anything to eliminate the possible use of the space.

"Now let's move on to the third 'S'."

3rd S - SWEEP

- ◆ Sweep the floors, wipe off the equipment, paint if necessary

- ◆ Part of the sweep strategy is to develop methods to prevent the accumulation of dirt, chips, shavings, and dust

- ◆ Establish an area where cleaning supplies are kept

- ◆ Use a ceiling down strategy

Mike continued, "Once we've sorted and straightened out the area, it's time for a good cleaning."

"You gotta be kidding," said Wendell. "I've been operating that mill for over ten years now and it's never been clean."

"Well, it's about time we changed that," said Mike. "Joe, you've already been on a 5S event. Wouldn't you rather work in a clean area?"

"Of course I would, who wouldn't?"

Randall, shaking his head in disagreement interrupted. "Man, it's goin' to take a whole lot of work to get that place clean, and for what? It'll never stay that way. I'm not bustin my butt for nothin'."

"I agree with Randall," said Hubert. "With chips flying everywhere and wey lube going all over the place, it'll be impossible to keep it clean."

Joe, why don't you finish what you were about to say," asked Mike. "What happened on the 5S you were on?"

"We all felt the way Randall feels. It seemed like an impossible task. But we did it. Not only that, but the work center's been clean ever since the 5S. Believe me, after bustin' my butt cleaning it, I'll give the guys hell if they don't keep it that way. I didn't do all that work for nothing."

Joe was a credible source, so Mike encouraged him to continue. "How about the operators Joe, what did they think?"

"You mean after the event?"

"Yeah."

"At first they didn't know what to make of it. Sure, they liked working in a clean work center, but they thought it'd never stay that way. We had a good laugh from Tony because his wife thought he'd been laid off but wasn't telling her."

"I don't get it," said Wendell. "Why did his wife think he was laid off?"

"Tony was coming home from work a lot cleaner than usual and his wife didn't believe he still had the same job. It wasn't until he brought home his paycheck that she finally believed him. Who would've thought being clean could cause a problem, but it did for Tony."

Everyone laughed except for Randall; he wasn't buying any of it. Mike knew he'd just have to give Randall time; he certainly wasn't going to accept all of this on the basis of one event or some funny stories. Randall was a long-term project.

Mike repeated the question he asked earlier, hoping for support from the group. "Wouldn't you rather work in a clean place than in a filthy one?" Most of the group nodded in agreement. "Of course you would—it's human nature. Let me ask one more question. Do you think you'd get better quality out of a clean shop or one that's a filthy mess?"

"C'mon Mike, that's obvious," responded Paul as he stared disappointingly at Mike.

"Well, what's the answer then, Paul?"

"Of course quality will be better in a clean shop."

"Why?" pressed Mike.

"Because if it's filthy it's hard to produce a clean, high quality part. The tooling will be filthy, the fixtures will be filthy, and the machine will be a mess. Dirt, dust, chips, and shavings might damage the part or cause a dimensional tolerance issue. It has to affect quality."

"You bet it will," said Mike, as he walked across the front of the room with a little more hop in his step. "How about safety? Is a filthy work area as safe as a clean one?"

"Probably not," said Anthony.

"Probably?" questioned Mike. "C'mon Anthony, tell me why."

"Well, if it's a dirty mess there are probably more trip hazards."

"Now you're talking. What else?"

"Flying dust, dirt, and shavings from a filthy work area can get into an operator's eyes."

"But that's why we wear safety glasses," argued Randall.

"But even safety glasses aren't foolproof," responded Mike. "Wouldn't you agree that the dirtier the work area, the greater the chance of eye injury?"

"That makes sense, and I don't need to work in the machine shop to understand that," said Josh.

Mike wasn't finished. He knew that most people still didn't understand why the place had to be cleaned up. He realized he had to explain it over and over, not only in this class, but continuously, until it became a way of life for everyone, both in the shop and the office.

"And how about the equipment? Do you think the equipment will last longer in a clean, or filthy, work environment? What do you think Christy?"

"I know our computer systems wouldn't be reliable if we let the servers become a mess, so I assume it's the same with our equipment in the shop. Heck, they're loaded with electronics."

"You're not kidding," said Anthony, thinking about the maintenance implications. "My job's a lot easier if the equipment is kept up."

"How about from another perspective, Anthony? How hard is it to spot a small leak under layers of filth and grime?" asked Mike.

"We never see the small leaks. We only notice it when it becomes a major problem and there's a puddle on the floor."

"Precisely," said Mike, forwarding to his next slide.

True Value of Sweep

- ◆ Clean to Inspect

- ◆ Inspect to Detect

- ◆ Detect to Correct

- ◆ In essence, putting operation under a microscope like never before!

You have to constantly repeat this. It's very difficult for the workplace to fully grasp this!

"The cleaning process is also an opportunity to fully inspect the work center. I can't tell you how many 5S events I've been in where we've found reservoirs that needed to be maintained but no one knew they existed or filters that were so covered in dirt and grime you couldn't even find them. So let me ask you this: if a clean work area leads to better quality, improved safety, and I'll add, improved morale, why haven't we bothered to keep it clean?"

"That's the easiest question you've asked so far," said Hubert smiling and turning toward Paul. "Do you think we have time to clean our areas? Hell no! We have to get our hours off the machines every day or else."

Paul stiffened right up. "You know how long it would take to clean like that every day? It'd

be ridiculous! We can't spend all our time cleaning and still make schedule."

"You can keep it that clean and still make
schedule," responded Mike. "But you have to
make it easier to keep it clean. That's the key.
So when you go through the cleaning process
over the next couple of days, I want you all to
think about how to make the cleaning process
much easier. If that means we'll have to build
containment devices or hoppers, or whatever,
so be it. Removing all the junk from the area
and straightening out what's left also will make
it a lot easier. Let me show you some slides to
explain."

Mike went through about fifteen slides of
before and after pictures, illustrating hoppers
that catch waste material rather than letting it
just fall on the floor, guarding to contain chips,
racks to easily organize and identify parts, and
all sorts of tricks to make cleaning easier. Mike
also emphasized that anything that can move
should be on wheels to facilitate cleaning. Everything else should be attached to posts or to
the machine, and put as close as possible to the
point of use. A lot of questions were addressed and
Mike felt this part of the class went reasonably well.

"Okay, I understand, but how can we possibly keep it clean every day?" asked Wendell. "I'd
like to work in a cleaner area. Heck, who
wouldn't? But it seems like it'll take so long."

"I agree with Wendell; you're asking a lot.
Hell, I can't even keep my office clean and I don't

have chips flying around," said Jack, in support of the operators.

"Ain't that the truth," said Josh. "Your office is a pig pen. We should be 5S'ing Jack's area, not Wendell's"

"Sounds like we have a great candidate for our first marketing 5S. We'll have to put that on our Lean schedule," said Mike. "But let's get back to Wendell's question. It's a great segue into the fourth 'S', *Schedule.*"

4th S - Schedule

♦ **Standardize and maintain the use of sort, straighten, and sweep**

♦ **Use a checklist by area**

♦ **The idea is to clean up while the task is small—daily by shift**

"To clean the area quickly, we'll need a standard process that the operators will have to follow religiously. As part of this event, a couple of you will develop a schedule which will list everything that has to be cleaned and the frequency. Some items will be done daily, some once a week, and others perhaps less frequently. For those items that need to be done only once a week, they'll be spread out so each day something different is done. This will minimize the time it takes to clean each day, yet ensure everything gets done."

Mike felt the group was getting overloaded on the cleaning topic. The best learning would occur when they were out on the shop floor doing the work. It was time to move on to the 5th 'S', *Sustain*, so he could wrap up the classroom training.

5th S - Sustain

♦ **Develop Discipline**

♦ **Sustain means making the first 4 S's a habit, and part of the plants culture**

♦ **Have a team evaluate and grade the 5S implementation throughout the plant**

♦ **Review all areas monthly**

♦ **Post Results**

"Even though it might not seem like it, achieving the first 4 S's is the easy part. The tough part is sustaining the first 4 S's. . ."

"No kidding," interrupted Joe. "We worked our butts off in Work Center 222, and it didn't take long for it to start getting messy again."

"Man, I'm not doing all this work for nothing," said Josh. "I could be working on my engineering projects instead of wasting my time on something that won't be maintained."

"Don't worry Josh, it got better. It just took some time," responded Joe.

"Sustaining the first 4 S's is accomplished in a number of ways," continued Mike. "Once this area is completed, we'll establish a regular audit schedule to grade the work center. A numerical score will be provided, as well as three suggestions to encourage continuous improvement. These will be reviewed with the operators each month."

"Is the score gonna be used against me?" asked Randall.

"The audit's provided to help continuously improve the process."

"Cut the BS! Will it affect my pay?"

"Eventually it'll be factored into the merit increase process. We need to become world class to compete and we want—no, I mean we have to—encourage the appropriate processes."

That got everyone's attention. Mike didn't want to get into the pay issue, but he also hated to avoid direct questions. He learned that the truth was always the best course of action. And it didn't hurt to let out hints that eventually the pay system would have to change to be in alignment with Lean.

"What else do we have to do to sustain?" asked Paul, fidgeting uncomfortably in his seat.

"You'll play a big part. You're their supervisor."

"What do you mean?"

"Paul, if you don't take an interest in the work centers after they've been 5S'd, then why should the operators care about sustaining? We've done 5S in a couple of other areas in the machine shop. Have you been checking their 5S scores, congratulating them when they improve, reviewing the audit suggestions with the operators, and so on?"

"You gotta be kidding. I've tried, but I just can't find the time. I'm constantly chasing down parts and answering questions, I don't have the time."

"You have to make time. If we're ever going to improve and make your job easier, we have to get past the 5S's. It's really the ticket to play in the Lean journey. I can't emphasize that enough. If we can't do something as simple as 5S, we'll never be in a position to do any of the other improvements, like set-up reduction, TPM, etc."

"Can't we just do set-up reductions first? Then we can see some real improvements."

"I guarantee you'll see a reduction in set-up times as a result of this 5S."

"Why?" asked Josh, sitting up and paying attention now. The mechanical engineer was curious as to how the process could be improved.

Mike couldn't help himself from getting on Josh's case at this point. "Josh, you're an engineer, you understand the processes, right?"

"I like to think so."

"Good. How do you estimate the cost of a new part you're designing?"

"I look for a similar part that we've made before, and then check the run times and set-up times for that part. Then I make adjustments based on the differences of the new part and come up with a best guess."

"So then you add up the run time and set-up time and multiply it by the work center rate and add the material cost to get the total estimated cost?"

"That's it," agreed Josh.

"Fred, does that make sense to you?"

"Sure does, we've always done it that way."

"Josh, do you ever go out into the shop and actually watch the part being machined?"

"Not really."

"So then you haven't ever watched a set-up from start to finish?"

"No. I've walked by from time to time, but I don't have time to watch an entire set-up. It could take an hour or so."

"Then you'll be astonished to find out that the simple process of 5S'ing a work center can cut set-ups by up to fifty percent."

"How could it do that?" challenged Wendell.

"By eliminating all the wasted time looking for material, tooling, and a whole bunch of other stuff."

"That's hard to believe," said Christy.

"I'll tell you what; we're going to prove it as part of this event. One thing I insist on for every event is what I call the 'Just the Facts' section. Here's what I mean. Paul worked with the operators and industrial engineering to collect the info." Mike forwarded to the next slide.

Just the Facts

- ◆ Set-up Times   56 Mins.
- ◆ Set-ups per annum   1,000
- ◆ Set-ups hrs./annum   933 hrs.
- ◆ Square feet   600 sq. ft.
- ◆ Scrap per labor hour $4.00

The slide got the attention of everyone, including Randall. "Wow, that's almost six months of work settin' up the machine. You gotta be kiddin'."

"I didn't realize it takes almost an hour to set up one part," added Christy, somewhat incredulously.

"Hey, what's the big deal? That's not unusual in a machine shop," replied Paul defensively.

"It's not unusual at all," added Harold. "Heck, I've been supplying that work center with tooling for years and it's always been that way. . ."

Mike couldn't contain himself. "That's the point!"

"What is?" asked Harold.

"That everyone accepts a 56-minute set-up because it's always been that way. Josh, you use that set-up time to estimate the cost of a new part. Fred, if the new part performs to standard, which is now 56 minutes plus or minus Josh's esteemed wisdom, it's okay by you. Harold, you see nothing wrong with the status quo, and Paul, you compare what we do to other machine shops and we're all the same, so it's okay. The point is that the status quo is no longer acceptable. To compete in the global marketplace, we have to get better every day and 5S is as good a place as any to start. So, after we finish this event, we'll record the set-up times to see if we've improved."

"I'm confused," said Hubert. "I thought at one of our plant meetings you said we'd be doing set-up events and film the process. Isn't that when we improve set-ups?"

"That's a good question; thanks for bringing it up. If we filmed the set-up now, the operators would hardly be in the film as they would spend most of their time walking around to get materials and tooling. That's the wasted time the 5S will eliminate. You really need to do the 5S first, and then the set-up reduction event afterwards, to focus on the process."

"Makes sense," said Josh nodding approval.

"By the way, Josh, based on your estimate of the cost of a new part, wouldn't you and industrial engineering decide to buy the part on the outside if you could purchase it for less than we could make it?"

"Absolutely, why wouldn't we?"

"Because it's the easy way out. We're just putting margin and work hours in someone else's shop because we're not working on the real opportunity, reducing set-up times. So you can see how important set-up times are, and 5S is the first step in the improvement process."

Mike took a sip of water and paused for a minute to let his message sink in.

"Now, let's talk about the soft benefits of having a 5S'd plant. How would you feel about eating in a restaurant if you noticed that the kitchen was a filthy mess?"

"That's a stupid question," said Wendell in his raspy voice.

"You're right. How would you feel about having surgery in a dirty hospital? Not too comfortable I bet. So how do you think our customers feel about touring a messy plant?"

"I never thought about that," said Joe.

"We all should. At one place I worked, a customer told me he placed a large order with us rather than the competition because our plant was so neat and orderly while the competitor's plant was a mess. The customer said that after seeing both plants, he just wasn't confident the competitor would be in business in five or ten years to service his product. The plant was part of the buying decision for this particular customer, just like the cleanliness of a restaurant would certainly enter our buying decision for a meal.

"One last thing regarding the sustain process. Here's how we'll really know if we're sustaining." Mike forwarded to the next slide.

5S Sustain Measure

One Measure:

♦ **Eliminating special clean-ups for customer visits—always being "tour or visit ready"**

"Okay, we're done with the presentation part of the event. Let's take a short break and then we'll head out into the plant. Let's meet back here in ten minutes, and don't forget to bring your safety glasses."

Mike glanced at his watch. It was ten minutes to ten, which meant he was already twenty minutes behind schedule. He realized this was going to be a very challenging group.

As everyone was leaving, Fred approached Mike.

"Boy, the aggressive, takes no prisoners Mike is starting to come out again."

"Was I that bad?"

"Borderline. The operators were getting offended by your comments, and I don't blame them. It's like you're blaming them for the lack of improvement."

"Maybe I came off that way a little bit. But I did mention that it's the process, not the operator, and that's the truth. I just get so frustrated when I hear everyone say it's always been like that and they're content with it. They'll get over it. At least I think I got their attention when it became clear their jobs may be at risk."

"Mike, they're no different than anyone else. Look how much trouble you had with me and the changes we needed to make in accounting. Now don't go and piss them off like you did me. Hell, it's a miracle we became friends. And besides, you're in charge of manufacturing, so it's your fault, not theirs."

"Thanks for the feedback. You're right. We haven't done that much in the machine shop yet so I guess I'll need to be a little more patient."

The machine operators, Joe, Wendell, and Hubert sat together in the company cafeteria discussing the class.

"Joe, you did this before, what do you think?

Is he crazy or what?" asked Hubert.

"Mike's an okay guy. He just has this thing for cleaning up the place."

"How about reducing set-ups? Does it work?" asked Wendell.

"Can't really say," said Joe. "I think it's better, but who knows. Mike was ripped at the session I was at because Paul didn't have any facts to share. So who knows? He must've read him the riot act because they had the numbers today."

"I guess we'll find out in a few weeks then," said Hubert, wiping the coffee from his mustache.

"What's the big deal about set-ups anyway?" noted Wendell. "If they just give us bigger batches to run, set-ups wouldn't be a problem."

"Ain't that the truth," responded Hubert as the other two nodded in agreement.

Chapter 6
Orange Vests
& Work Center Visit
Day 1 (10:00 A.M.)

When everyone returned to the room, there were orange vests waiting for them at their tables. Most of the folks from the plant were familiar with the routine but the office participants had no idea what the vest was all about.

"What's this for?" asked Josh.

"You're going to look great in it," said Joe, laughing as he put on his vest.

"How about just telling me what it's for."

"Sure thing. Mike has us wear the vests for three reasons and it really works."

As Joe was talking, Mike flipped to the slide on the orange vests.

Orange Vests

Orange Vests are used to:

♦ Let everyone know that something special is taking place

♦ Let everyone know who is participating in the event

♦ Make it easier to find your team-mates during the event

"Josh, you'll get used to it in no time and won't even realize you're wearing it. You'll see. It really is a big help," said Joe.

"Why is it so important for everyone to know who's participating?" asked Hubert.

"Care to answer that, Harold?" asked Mike.

"I'll just tell you what I think."

"Sure, go ahead."

"I like to see who's involved and the vest makes it easy. There's a real buzz around the plant when we see one of the big honchos from the office wearing a vest."

"Why is that?" pressed Mike.

"Because if we start seeing vice presidents

and directors out here, we'll know it's serious. Otherwise, it's just another program for the manufacturing grunts to do."

"Do you all feel that way?" asked Fred.

A chorus of yeses followed from the manufacturing folks in the room.

"There's one more benefit, although I don't like to put it on the slide," added Mike. "As the event proceeds, you'll need help from some of the other areas in the shop, either to make something, to paint something, or whatever. When you ask for that help, you're usually treated a little better as everyone knows you're on a tight time schedule."

"So why don't you put that in the slide?" asked Christy.

"Because I don't necessarily want that to be the case. I don't want the other folks jeopardizing their schedules to help because they think the vest is a license to drop everything else and assist you. So make sure that doesn't happen if you do seek out help."

"Makes sense," responded Christy. She was beginning to think this was a well-thought-out process.

"Okay, it's time to get going. Everyone put on your vests and let's head out to the shop floor. First, we'll spend some time at the work centers that've already been 5S'd so you'll have a better idea of what we need to do. Then we'll head over to Work Center 111 where I'd like each of you to make a list of the things that you think need to be done, and the waste that you see. I have clipboards and pads for everyone. Just list everything and then we'll come back and brainstorm the ideas. Once we get to Work Center 111, you'll have thirty minutes to complete your assessments. Then let's all meet back up here at eleven o'clock to go through it. Any questions?"

Everyone raised their hands. Mike was trying to save time and get back on schedule, but it was obvious they were all confused by his short explanation.

"What do you mean by things that have to be done?" called out Wendell.

"What detail do you want?" asked Josh.

"What exactly am I supposed to do?" asked Jack.

"I'm just asking you to write down what we can improve. You'll get a much better idea after we tour the other areas. I'll be there to help and so will Joe. It's really very easy, so don't worry about it."

Mike headed out of the room and asked everyone to follow him. They took fifteen minutes and toured a few other work centers and spoke with the operators. They also saw the before and after 5S pictures hanging at the work stations. There was a lot of discussion amongst the team and it seemed as if they were getting a better idea of what had to be done. Then Mike asked everyone to follow him to Work Center 111. Once there, Mike reminded them of the assignment.

"Take thirty minutes and list all the improvements you think we should make at the work center, based on the class material and what you saw at the other work centers. If you have any questions, ask the operators, Joe and Wendell. They are the area experts for the event."

"How 'bout giving us an example?" asked Harold.

"Okay, you could write down that the tools should be located closer to the point of use, or that the junk not being used should be removed, or that the material should be better organized. Just look around and see what would prevent the operator from doing the best job possible via the elimination of waste. Compare this work center to the 5S'd work centers, as well as to the pictures I showed you in the Training Room. List what we have to do to make this one as organized and effective. Ask the operators what tools they use, where the fixtures should be located for ease of use, what items are used most frequently, what problems they have, questions like that."

"Okay, I got it. Is that all you want us to do?"

"That's it, Harold." Mike glanced at his watch. "See you all back in the Training Room at eleven o'clock sharp."

CHAPTER 7

BRAINSTORMING AT WORK CENTER 111

DAY 1 (10:35 A.M.)

"Josh, you writing anything down?" asked Jack.

"I guess we'd better," responded Josh, looking around to see what everyone else was doing.

"Sounds pretty stupid to me. I can't believe we have to do this crap."

Josh pointed toward Randall. "Look at him, he's just wandering around,"

"Yeah, you know he's dreading every minute of this."

"I bet he doesn't make it to the end."

"Hell, I'm worried how I'm going to make it. I can't believe I got an MBA so I could walk around the shop taking notes about how dirty it is."

Christy walked by and interrupted them. "Hey, why don't you guys get busy?"

"Are you really taking this seriously Christy?" asked Josh, somewhat amazed.

"I have to admit, I don't know what to make of it, but as long as we're out here we might as well do what Mike says."

"Why? He's not my boss." protested Jack.

"He's not mine either."

"Yeah, but Fred's on the team and you have to answer to him."

"Why don't you let me finish, Jack?"

"Okay, okay, I'm sorry. Go ahead."

"It's not just about Fred. You heard Peter. He said everyone has to take part in an event, so we might as well get it over with."

"C'mon Christy, that's bull," responded Jack emphatically. "It's easy for Peter to tell everyone we have to be in an event, but have you seen him do it yet? It's good enough for all of us but he's not walking the talk."

"You know how busy Peter is. He's got the board, the banks, the customers, and everyone else to deal with. He's on the road all the time. I'm sure he'll be part of an event as soon as he gets a chance."

"We're all busy, so I don't buy it," said Jack as he turned and walked away from Christy.

She was about to go after Jack when Josh grabbed her by the shoulder. "Let him cool down. He'll be okay."

"I hope so. We've just started this event. We have a long way to go."

"So tell me, what do you really think about this?" asked Josh, milking every minute he could spend with Christy.

"I'm willing to give it a chance. Mike's done some incredible things in purchasing. He must know what he's doing out here."

"Look who's had a change of heart," needled Josh. "I heard you weren't too excited about being on the team."

"No, I wasn't, but I'm going to make the best out of it. And we don't have much time left, so we might as well finish making up our lists."

"I guess so."

Christy walked away and started to jot some things down on her clipboard.

About ten minutes had passed when Mike came back to see how everyone was doing. He looked at Randall's blank sheet of paper on his clipboard. "Randall, need some help?"

"Nah."

"You haven't written anything down yet."

"I know. Don't see the point."

"You'll never see the point if you don't start participating. I'm not going to force you to do this. If you want out, let me know now; otherwise I expect you to be part of the team."

"If I gotta write a few things down to get a free lunch, I'll do it."

I could care less why he participates, as long as he does it, thought Mike. If I can just get him to make it through Wednesday, he'll understand what it's all about. It happens almost every time.

Mike spent a few minutes taking digital pictures of the area. He wanted some "before" pictures that captured the filthiest areas, safety issues, and anything else that would provide the greatest impact when compared with the "after" pictures. He usually took about a dozen pictures.

CHAPTER 8
BRAINSTORMING PART 1

DAY 1 (11:00 A.M.)

Everyone headed back to the training room. As they took their seats, Mike went to the front of the room, stood next to a flip chart, and began to explain the next steps in the process.

"Now we're going to brainstorm all the ideas you came up with to eliminate the waste in Work Center 111."

"What do you mean by brainstorm?" asked Harold.

"Brainstorming is a valuable tool for starting discussions, collecting lots of ideas, and getting everyone involved in the process. Here's exactly what we're going to do." Mike removed a pad covering the front lens of the PowerPoint projector to expose the brainstorming slide.

Brainstorming

Brainstorming Process:

♦ State the problem in the form of a question.

♦ Go around the room and ask each person to provide one idea. When everyone has had a turn, go around the room again and continue until all ideas have been exhausted.

♦ If you don't have an idea, simply say pass and we'll move on to the next person.

"So what's the question, Mike?" asked Hubert.

Mike responded, "What can we do to eliminate the waste at Work Center 111? You've all written down some things. Now I'm going to make a list and record each item on the flip charts. But before we go around the room, I want to explain a few rules of the process." Mike flipped to the next slide.

Brainstorming Rules

♦ **No idea will be dismissed.**

♦ **No judgment of any idea during the process.**

♦ **No laughing, criticizing, or making fun of any idea.**

♦ **Piggybacking of ideas is encouraged.**

"What fun is it if we can't laugh at some of the ideas?" asked Randall. "I saw what some folks were writin' and it made no sense to me."

"We want to make sure we don't leave any ideas out," responded Mike. "We may not do everything we list, but that'll be the team's decision. In the meantime, we don't want to leave any stone unturned. What might seem like a bad idea to you might make a lot of sense to someone else, so let's not be critical."

"What does piggybacking mean?" asked Christy.

"That's when someone provides an idea and you have something you'd like to add to perhaps expand the idea and give it a different twist. It's a way of insuring we get everything. We hope someone else's ideas will get you to think of something that might not be on your list. So let's get started." Mike turned towards his left and looked at Christy. "I guess you get to start us off again. What would you like to put on the list?"

"How about cleaning out all the cabinets? It's a real mess out there."

Joe crossed his arms, leaned back, and turned toward Christy, "You don't need to call my area a mess."

"Joe's right," said Mike quickly defusing the issue. "We want to put our ideas on the flip chart but we don't need to criticize. I'm sure if we went to any work area in the shop, or in the office, we'd find a mess. So let's stick to the ideas, please."

Christy turned toward Joe who was seated diagonally across from her. "Sorry about that, Joe."

Joe simply nodded back at her.

Mike turned to the flip chart and wrote down, *"clean out all cabinets."*

"How about just removing the cabinet?" asked Harold. "I looked inside and you don't need all those tools at the work center. Heck, I could use them in the tool crib."

"No way! I need them," objected Joe.

"Remember the rules, Joe," reminded Mike. "If you don't need them in the next thirty days, we should take them out of the work center."

"Hey, that's easy for you to say, but then I'll never have the right tool when I need it."

"Let's not argue every point. Let's finish going around the room and put every idea up and then we'll decide what we need to do."

Mike served as both the facilitator and as a member of the team and contributed ideas each time his turn came up.

"Your turn, Josh."

"How about making a set-up cart?"

"That's fine. Jack, your turn."

"We need to label everything at the work center."

Mike continued around the room and was up to Wendell for the third time when the fireworks started again.

"Let's get rid of the ball screw," said Wendell.

"Hey, don't go doin' that," shot back Anthony. "That thing's brand new; we need to put it on the machine."

"It's just sittin' in the corner getting in the way of everything," responded Wendell. "You heard the rules. If it hasn't been used recently it's in the way and waste."

"Okay guys, let's put it on the board and we'll discuss it later. This is just the brainstorming part and we need to get through it." Mike added it to the list. Anthony shook his head in disgust.

The brainstorming continued for another fifteen minutes until lunch was delivered at eleven thirty. Five sheets were already taped to the walls with 35 ideas listed.

"Ah, you got us a gourmet lunch, I see," said Jack as he got up to help unload the pizza and sodas from the delivery cart.

"You'll just have to lower yourself to eat with us shop folks," needled Harold. "We know it's not up to the standards of a marketing department lunch."

"Yeah, but at least we're going to get an hour and a half for lunch like we do everyday in marketing," shot back Jack. "Isn't that right Mike?"

"In your dreams Jack. Let's all get our lunch and finish up the brainstorming while we're eating. We're behind schedule and it shouldn't take too long to wrap up this part."

There was a lot of moaning and groaning about Mike's request. Just about everyone got their lunch and returned to their seats to continue with the session. Fred left briefly to check his phone messages and e-mail, Paul left for ten minutes to check on the shop, and Randall was nowhere to be seen.

After about fifteen minutes, Mike heard Barb Bonner, the Human Resources Manager, page him on the company intercom. He excused himself, reached over to the phone and dialed her extension.

"Barb, what's up?"

"Can I see you for a second?"

"Now? I'm right in the middle of a 5S."

"I know that, but it's really important. I need to see you now."

"I can't believe this. I'll be right over."

Mike excused himself from the class and headed over to Human Resources. He was pretty upset that Barb would interrupt him. Barb and Mike had a good relationship and Mike respected her for the support she provided since he joined Tricor. The Lean transformation had put a lot of the human resource policies under question and Barb dealt with each issue with an open mind. She knew better than to bother him during an event, though. It better be important, he thought.

Mike hustled down two flights of stairs and double timed it to the far end of the building and into Barb's office. "So what's so important that I had to leave the 5S event?"

"Mike, sit down so we can talk about the event."

"What's there to talk about?" Mike was clearly agitated and refused Barb's offer to sit down.

"Randall was just in to see me and he was pretty upset."

"He's got an attitude problem and could care less about what we're doing."

"That may be the case, but he's got a legitimate complaint right now."

"And what's that?"

"You're making the team work through lunch."

"As long as we're all eating in the room anyway, I was just trying to get back on schedule. Nobody seemed to mind."

"If they did, you'd be the last person they'd complain to. The point is that some of them do mind and you need to give them time to eat. Especially the hourly folks who aren't being paid for their half-hour lunch breaks."

"C'mon, you know most of us work through lunch anyway. What's the big deal? We've done this at one time or another in just about every event and no one ever complained."

"Until now."

"That's just Randall, and you know he's a head case anyway."

"He may be difficult, but he does his job. We've got to do ours as well and honor the work rules. So please, give the team their thirty-minute lunch break and let them eat wherever they want."

Mike grabbed his pad from Barb's desk and left her office. He knew she was right, but it was just one employee that was making it difficult for everyone.

As he was leaving, Barb called out to him, "Don't take this out on Randall."

"I won't," he responded and left in a huff.

Mike returned to the class and let everyone know they would resume the brainstorming session at twelve-thirty. Everyone had finished their lunch by now so they all bolted out of the room except Fred.

"Why the change of heart," asked Fred

"Randall complained to Barb that I'm chaining everyone to their desks and he wants his half-hour for lunch."

"Mike, I know you don't want to hear this, but Randall's right. We both know that we have a lot of lunch meetings with salaried personnel and that's often part of the job, but you can't do it with the hourly folks."

"That's why I wish everyone was equal. Just put everyone on salary and forget this class shit."

"Why, so you can work them to death?"

"Hell no. Just to demonstrate that we're all one team and live by the same rules. And if that occasionally means we all work through lunch, so be it. We've had some of our best discussions over lunch in the other events. And most of the time everybody decided to stay on their own and keep working."

"Well that's not the law, so forget it."

Mike grabbed a piece of pizza and soda and sat at one of the empty tables. Fred thought it best to leave him alone to cool off.

CHAPTER 9

BRAINSTORMING PART 2

DAY 1 (12:30 P.M.)

Just about everyone returned to the room at about twelve-thirty as Mike had instructed them. Randall, the last team member to return, was laughing and horsing around with Hubert as they came into the room. Mike did everything he could to contain himself.

"Okay, let's try to wrap this up in fifteen minutes. We have a lot to do before we adjourn today." Mike continued to solicit ideas by going around the table. Some of the team members were out of ideas, so Mike started asking for suggestions from anyone. When all the ideas had been exhausted, there were forty-nine ideas spread across seven sheets of flip-chart paper taped up along an entire wall. Mike always made sure to put the flip charts along one wall, if possible. Otherwise later, when the voting would take place, items could be overlooked if the charts were separated.

Mike was pleased with the list of ideas. He had been conducting brainstorming sessions for many years and about ninety percent of the time there were between forty and fifty ideas listed. He thought it was some higher law of brainstorming that was invoked each session whereby you always got about four or five ideas per participant. He used the idea count as a metric to see if the group was engaged. If the idea count was significantly below forty ideas, then he'd encourage the group to think of additional items and help them as best as possible. Fortunately that was not the case this time.

Brainstorming Ideas - Work Center 111

1. Clean out all cabinets
2. Return tools to tool crib
3. Make set-up cart
4. Sort items and Red Tag
5. Chips everywhere—clean up
6. Provide a place for cleaning supplies
7. Clean walls
8. Repaint machine a light color
9. Make coolant collection trays
10. Mark staging area
11. Mount retractable hose reel near point of use
12. Routings should reference tooling locations
13. Remove fixtures belonging to other work centers
14. Provide hanger for mounting prints
15. Mount computer on column
16. Provide set-up visuals
17. Make bulletin board
18. Prepare TPM Schedule
19. Minimize trips to tool crib
20. Set up tooling kanban
21. Standardize material handling equipment
22. Need two tooling racks, one mounted on machine
23. Build set-up cart on wheels
24. Eliminate tool chests
25. Provide fixture pictures on set-up sheets
26. Build chip guards
27. Identify finished goods in work center
28. Eliminate clocking on and off jobs—it's waste
29. Mark and label all tools
30. Group tooling by common use on top cabinet in holders
31. Location of fixture pallets—color coded or numbered by machine
32. Clean entire area
33. Minimize trips to tool crib
34. New ball screw for machine (it's in house)
35. Get dedicated crane
36. Get new floor mat for operator
37. Make set-up tools mobile
38. Re-evaluate all tools kept at machine and relocate to point of use
39. Provide a home for lifting straps and magnet
40. Cover pockets at base of machine
41. Post set-up procedures
42. Make troughs for way lube
43. Make a shim box and organize
44. Provide retractable barrier to collect/redirect chips
45. Remove air line that is a tripping hazard
46. Provide a convenient holder for drawings
47. Organize file cabinet
48. Remove junk on top of machine
49. Add power tools

"Now what do we do?" asked Christy, always the curious one.

"The team's going to decide the most important items by voting. And the suggestions with the most votes are the ones we'll work on for the next two-and-a-half days."

"A lot of the items are similar to each other," Fred pointed out.

"You're right. We're going to group like items first," responded Mike. "We don't want to vote until we have done some sorting and I need everyone's help to do it. We'll start with the first item. What other items on the list are similar to the first item, *Cleaning out all the cabinets*?"

"How about number 32, is that what you mean?" asked Harold.

"Exactly. I'll cross off number 32 and write that next to number 1. So this way if you vote for number 1, you'll also be voting for number 32. We don't want to waste our votes by voting on the same thing five times."

"How about number 48, that goes with number 1," called out Fred.

The group took about ten minutes to complete the entire list as follows:

Brainstorming Ideas—Work Center 111

4,6,7,32,47,48, 1. Clean out all cabinets
13,19,20,22,24,29,30,33,38,49, 2. Return tools to tool crib
23,37, 3. Make set-up cart
~~4~~. Sort items and Red Tag
26,40,44, 5. Chips everywhere - clean up
~~6~~. Provide a place for cleaning supplies
~~7~~. Clean walls
8. Repaint machine a light color
42, 9. Make coolant collection trays
21,27,31, 10. Mark staging area
45, 11. Mount retractable hose reel near point of use
12. Routings should reference tooling locations
~~13~~. Remove fixtures belonging to other work centers
15,16,17,25,41,46, 14. Provide hanger for mounting prints
~~15~~. Mount computer on column
~~16~~. Provide set-up visuals
~~17~~. Make bulletin board
18. Prepare TPM Schedule
~~19~~. Minimize trips to tool crib
~~20~~. Set up tooling kanban
~~21~~. Standardize material handling equipment
~~22~~. Need two tooling racks, one mounted on machine
~~23~~. Build set-up cart on wheels
~~24~~. Eliminate tool chests
~~25~~. Provide fixture pictures on set-up sheets
~~26~~. Build chip guards
~~27~~. Identify finished goods in work center
28. Eliminate clocking on and off jobs—it's waste
~~29~~. Mark and label all tools
~~30~~. Group tooling by common use on top cabinet
   in holders
~~31~~. Location of fixture pallets—color coded or
   numbered by machine
~~32~~. Clean entire area
~~33~~. Minimize trips to tool crib
34. New ball screw for machine (it's in house)
35. Get dedicated crane
36. Get new floor mat for operator
~~37~~. Make setup tools mobile
~~38~~. Re-evaluate all tools kept at machine and relocate
   to point of use
39. Provide a home for lifting straps and magnet
~~40~~. Cover pockets at base of machine
~~41~~. Post set-up procedures
~~42~~. Make troughs for way lube
43. Make a shim box and organize
~~44~~. Provide retractable barrier to collect/redirect chips
~~45~~. Remove air line that is a tripping hazard
~~46~~. Provide a convenient holder for drawings
~~47~~. Organize file cabinet
~~48~~. Remove junk on top of machine
~~49~~. Add power tools

Mike handed out yellow sticky notes to everyone and took one for himself.

"What's this for?" asked Wendell.

"We're going to vote on which items are the most important to work on. It'll be a team decision. But remember, we're voting on what we need to do for the 5S, not what we'd personally like to do. Everybody gets five votes."

"Can we vote for the same item more than once?" asked Jack, finally showing some interest.

"No, one vote per item," responded Mike. "Also, if an item is crossed out, please don't vote for it as you'll just be wasting your vote." Mike had explained this nuance at every event, but no matter what he said, someone always wasted votes on crossed off items. "When you're finished just fold over the post it and I'll come around and collect them. You don't need to put your name on them."

After about five minutes, Mike collected all the sticky notes and set them aside. "Now it's time to go out to the work center and start red tagging everything that needs to be removed. Joe and Wendell are the area experts, so they have to give the okay to physically remove the items to the Red Tag area."

"So nothing moves unless we give the okay?" asked Joe, looking around the room to make sure everyone realized he was the boss.

"If it's pretty obvious that an item doesn't belong there or hasn't moved in years because it has five inches of dust on it, I think they can go ahead without you, Joe. But if in doubt, Joe and Wendell have to decide. Is that fair enough?"

Joe nodded his approval.

"Good. It shouldn't take too long. Once the red tagging is done, a few of you should move the stuff out while the rest of you start cleaning the work center. Everything you'll need is on the 5S cart. If you need anything else, Anthony will help you find it. And remember, start from the top, down."

"How about the results of the voting?" asked Christy.

"We'll go through that at three fifteen. Everyone come back up then and we'll go over the results." Mike glanced at his watch and was getting concerned about the time. It was already a quarter after one. He'd ask for overtime when they got together later. "Now let's get going as we're running out of time."

Everyone left and Mike sorted through the votes so he'd be ready for the group when they returned. He sorted everything on the computer and prepared handouts for the team. Usually he did this during lunch so he could be out in the shop helping with the sorting process but that would have to wait today.

CHAPTER 10
RED TAGGING OF ITEMS

DAY 1 (1:15 P.M.)

While Mike was sorting through the votes, the team divided into natural groups and started moving the obvious items to the Red Tag area. But not everything was obvious.

"Christy, why are you tagging my tool chest?" asked Wendell.

"Because it looks like you don't use most of the stuff in here."

"Those are my tools and they're all staying here."

"C'mon Wendell, you don't really need all of this. Look in this drawer; it looks like this stuff hasn't been used in years."

"Close that up."

"How the heck can you find anything in

here. . . "

"Christy tellin' you how to run the machine now, Wendell," said Randall with a huge grin. "Maybe she can show you how to use all your tools."

"What's going on over here?" interrupted Josh, trying to help Christy out.

"Nothin' at all, Josh. Christy just wants to move all of Wendell's tools out of here."

Josh looked at the tool chest and opened some of the drawers. "Gee Wendell, you must have a hundred tools in there. How many do you really use?"

"That's what I was curious about," said Christy.

"A lot," said Wendell as he closed the drawers and moved between Josh and the tool chest.

"Come on, Wendell," prodded Josh. "How about taking out the tools you use for this work center and setting them off to the side?"

"What's going on here?" said Mike as he approached the group. "We can't afford everyone just standing around. Let's get going."

"I'm not moving my tool chest out of here. If I have to use my tools, then I'm going to store them wherever I want and no one's telling me any different."

"What if we provided the tools?" asked Mike.

"Never happen—this place is too cheap."

"Well, let's see what it would take. Let's spread out all of the tools you regularly use on this skid. I'm not guaranteeing we'd ever buy all the tools, because you may be right, but just for grins, let's see." Mike placed a piece of cardboard on top of an empty skid and motioned for Wendell to start moving his tools. This was a critical moment and Mike knew it. By now, everyone else was watching as well.

Wendell went through all the drawers and placed about twenty-five tools on the skid. You could hardly notice that he had taken any items out of the tool chest.

"Joe, come on over here," yelled Mike. "You have a tool chest just like this, don't you?"

"Sure do."

"Do you use the same tools as Wendell?"

"Yep."

"How would you feel if we provided all the tools you needed?"

"What happens when I have to work at another work center? I always bring my tool chest with me."

"You won't need to if that work center has

all the tools it needs."

"It all sounds real good Mike, but you don't understand. I've had my tool chest since I was sixteen years old. If you take it away from me it would be like taking my right arm away."

"I'm not going to take it away. But perhaps we can try a little experiment. What if we built a tool cart with exactly what you need and the company provided the tools? You can keep your tool chest here just in case we miss anything or if you have to go to another work center to do a job. Can we at least try that?"

"As long as I have my tool chest here in case I need it, I don't care if you go out and buy all new tools."

"Great, how about you, Wendell? Would you try it also?"

"If Joe's goin' to do it I'll give it a try. But my tool chest is not goin' anywhere."

"That's a deal," said Mike.

"Does anyone know where Harold is?" asked Mike.

"Yeah, he's getting some cleaning supplies for us from the tool crib," responded Hubert.

Mike walked over to the tool crib to find Harold.

"Harold, I need you to do me a favor."

"What?"

"Get with Joe and Wendell and make up a list of all the tools they need to run their work center. Then let me know what it would cost to buy all new tools."

"Not a problem."

"Thanks."

Mike headed back to the work center and saw Fred, Joe, and Anthony in a heated discussion. Joe was putting a strap around the box that contained the ball screw so he could lift it with the crane and move it to the Red Tag area.

"What's going on?" asked Mike as he stepped between Joe and Anthony.

"I'm trying to convince Joe to leave the ball screw here so maintenance can install it next week," replied Anthony.

"So what's wrong with that, Joe?" asked Mike.

"That's bull. I'm moving this out just like you told us. It's been sitting here for about eight months now and it just gets in my way. It'll never get installed."

"How come it hasn't been installed?" asked Fred turning toward Anthony.

"You gotta be kidding," responded Anthony. "Machines are breaking all the time. We haven't had time to work on this yet. And besides, the machine's running, so it's not an emergency."

"If you didn't have time, why did you order the ball screw?" demanded Joe. "It cost over three thousand dollars and that sounds like a lot of waste to me."

"C'mon, Joe. When I ordered it I thought I was going to get right to it. . ."

"Sounds like lousy scheduling to me," interrupted Joe.

Mike heard enough. "Anthony, how about installing the ball screw right after the 5S? You'll never have a better opportunity to work on a clean machine."

"We'll squeeze it in if we can. I can't predict what will happen between now and next week though."

"Let's make it a priority," insisted Mike. "In the meantime, we'll move it to the Red Tag area just to get it out of the way. Is that okay with you Anthony?"

"I guess so."

"Go ahead and move it out, Joe, but note on the Red Tag that we'll be installing it next week so no one moves it anywhere else."

"Will do."

Once the incident was over, everyone went back to work. Some of the team members had started to clean the machine while others were moving stuff to the Red Tag area. Others were cleaning out the cabinets as well as sorting the tooling. There was plenty to keep everyone busy. Mike decided he better get ready for the daily wrap up and headed back to the meeting room. On the way, he asked Fred to make sure that everyone headed back upstairs on time for the fifteen minute wrap-up session.

CHAPTER 11
WRAP-UP SESSION

DAY 1 (3:15 P.M.)

Everyone returned to the meeting room at about three fifteen and took their seats. Mike was anxious to get going so he could finish by three thirty as promised. He didn't want to hear from Barb again.

"We have a few things to wrap up before we call it a day. First, let's go over the results of the vote." Mike handed out a sheet with the list of ideas in order of the number of votes. "We need to divide into sub-teams to get as much done as possible by the end of Wednesday."

Jack looked over the handout and asked somewhat incredulously, "Do you expect us to complete all this in the next two days?"

"No, so we'll work on the highest priority items first. Whatever doesn't get done this week will be completed over the next month or two, but we'll talk about that on Wednesday. Okay, who wants to volunteer for the sub-teams? If you are handy, volunteer for something that we have to build. If you're like Fred, then volunteer for something you can do, like cleaning." Everyone laughed.

Brainstorming Ideas - Work Center 111			
Improvement Activity	Category	Votes	Team Members
1. Clean out all cabinets 4. Sort Items and Red Tag 6. Provide a place for cleaning supplies 7. Clean walls 32. Clean entire area 47. Organize file cabinet 48. Remove junk on top of machine	Cleaning	9	
2. Return tools to tool crib 13. Remove fixtures belonging to other work centers 19. Minimize trips to the tool crib 20. Set up tooling kanban 22. Need two tooling racks, one mounted on machine 24. Eliminate tool chests 29. Mark and label all tools 30. Group tooling by common use on top cabinet in holders 33. Minimize trips to tool crib 38. Re-evaluate all tools kept at machine and relocate to point of use 49. Add power tools	Tooling	9	
3. Make set-up cart 23. Build set-up cart on wheels 37. Make set-up tools mobile	Set-up Cart	7	
5. Chips everywhere - clean up 26. Build chip guards 40. Cover pockets at base of machine 44. Provide retractable barrier to collect/redirect chips	Confine Chips	6	
8. Repaint machine a light color			
10. Mark staging areas 21. Standardize material handling equipment 27. Identify finished goods in work center 31. Location of fixture pallets - color coded or numbered by machine	Material Handling	6	
9. Make coolant collection trays 42. Make troughs for way lube	Control Fluids	6	
12. Routings should reference tooling locations			
14. Provide a hanger for mounting prints 15. Mount computer on column 16. Provide set-up visuals 17. Make bulletin board 41. Post set-up procedures 46. Provide a convenient holder for drawings 25. Provide fixture pictures on set-up sheets	Information	5	
11. Mount retractable hose reel near point of use 45. Remove air line that is a tripping hazard		2	
34. New ball screw for machine (it's in house) 18. Prepare TPM schedule 35. Get dedicated crane 36. Get new floor mat for operator 39 Provide a home for lifting straps and magnet 43. Make a shim box and organize 28. Eliminate clocking on and off jobs - it's waste		2 1 1 1 1	

One by one, the team members volunteered until everyone's name was assigned to a sub-team. Mike wrote the names on the flip chart already hanging on the easel. Each group was assigned an operator whose knowledge was critical to completing the task. Mike also explained how everyone would have to help the cleaning sub-team if they were going to complete the event by Wednesday afternoon.

The sub-teams were as follows:

Brainstorming Ideas - Work Center 111			
Improvement Activity	Category	Votes	Team Members
1. Clean out all cabinets 4. Sort Items and Red Tag 6. Provide a place for cleaning supplies 7. Clean walls 32. Clean entire area 47. Organize file cabinet 48. Remove junk on top of machine	Cleaning	9	Fred Christy Mike Hubert
2. Return tools to tool crib 13. Remove fixtures belonging to other work centers 19. Minimize trips to the tool crib 20. Set up tooling kanban 22. Need two tooling racks, one mounted on machine 24. Eliminate tool chests 29. Mark and label all tools 30. Group tooling by common use on top cabinet in holders 33. Minimize trips to tool crib 38. Re-evaluate all tools kept at machine and relocate to point of use 49. Add power tools	Tooling	9	Josh Joe Harrold Paul
3. Make set-up cart 23. Build set-up cart on wheels 37. Make set-up tools mobile	Set-up Cart	7	Jack Wendell
5. Chips everywhere - clean up 26. Build chip guards 40. Cover pockets at base of machine 44. Provide retractable barrier to collect/redirect chips	Confine Chips	6	Anthony Randall
8. Repaint machine a light color			
10. Mark staging areas 21. Standardize material handling equipment 27. Identify finished goods in work center 31. Location of fixture pallets - color coded or numbered by machine	Material Handling	6	
9. Make coolant collection trays 42. Make troughs for way lube	Control Fluids	6	
12. Routings should reference tooling locations			
14. Provide a hanger for mounting prints 15. Mount computer on column 16. Provide set-up visuals 17. Make bulletin board 41. Post set-up procedures 46. Provide a convenient holder for drawings 25. Provide fixture pictures on set-up sheets	Information	5	
11. Mount retractable hose reel near point of use 45. Remove air line that is a tripping hazard		2	
34. New ball screw for machine (it's in house) 18. Prepare TPM schedule 35. Get dedicated crane 36. Get new floor mat for operator 39. Provide a home for lifting straps and magnet 43. Make a shim box and organize 28. Eliminate clocking on and off jobs - it's waste		2 1 1 1 1	

109

It was about three-thirty now and the troops were getting antsy.

"Just a couple more things," said Mike. "At the end of each day we need to make a list of any supplies we need. I'll try and pick them up tonight to save time tomorrow. Does anyone have anything?"

Harold stood up and handed Mike a list. "Here's the information you asked about the tools. I checked into the prices with our local distributor and he has most of it in stock."

Mike glanced at the list and saw that the total expenditure would not be too bad. "Great, I'll try and get everything before I head home tonight. One last item. We're already behind, so tomorrow will probably be a long day. If you can work a couple of hours overtime, it would be appreciated. Just let me know first thing in the morning. Finally, if you can stay today, that would also be appreciated. That's all I have for today."

Just about everyone took their vests off and headed out. Anthony, Harold, and Joe were the exceptions and went back into the plant to continue working. Mike was glad he had some volunteers, even it was only three team members. But he didn't for a second think they volunteered because they enjoyed the 5S; he knew they were after the overtime pay and nothing more.

As soon as Josh got out of the room he sought out Jack. "Can you believe he's asking us to work until five-thirty now?"

"I'm telling you, the man's a maniac. We have a lot more important things to do," agreed Jack.

Mike had spent about half-an-hour organizing his materials when Fred returned to the room.

"Having fun yet, Fred?" Mike called out.

"It's quite an experience, I'll give you that. I came back to tell you what I found out about the ball screw."

"What do you mean?"

"I just wanted to check out what Joe said."

"And. . ."

"The guy was right on. We bought the ball screw eight-and-a-half months ago and it cost three thousand one hundred and fifty dollars."

"That's the hard facts, Fred. But what's really significant is Joe and Wendell have been operating the machine for over eight months with a worn ball screw while they've stared at the replacement sitting on the floor every day. Wouldn't that frustrate the hell out of you?"

"Sure would."

"And don't you think operating the machine

with a worn part affects quality and productivity?"

"I guess so."

"You'd better believe it does."

"So why did we let it go on for so long?"

"Good question. I doubt anyone knew about it other than Joe and Wendell. I'll make sure it's on the top of maintenance's list once this event is over, and they won't have a choice. If we don't install it next week, I'll have lost all credibility with the operators."

"The operators will appreciate that."

"So will our customers."

"I've got to go catch up on my e-mail. I'll see you tomorrow, Mike."

"Thanks. And do me a favor..."

"What now?"

"Plan on working in the shop until five-thirty tomorrow. We need to demonstrate that we're all in this together. If management doesn't show the commitment, why should anyone else?"

"Because we all have other jobs to do."

"What's more important than becoming a World Class company, Fred? And it starts with 5S. You have to make the sacrifice at some point."

"You're gonna kill me. I told you I'd support you, so I guess I have no choice. I hope the rest of the team stays late."

"I'll settle for half."

"You know, Mike, some of them are pretty down on the whole event. They complain about it to whoever will listen."

"Don't you think I know that? It's par for the course."

"Is it always like this?"

"You betcha. Let me show you another slide that I don't share with the team." Mike flipped through his stack of papers and pulled out a laminated slide.

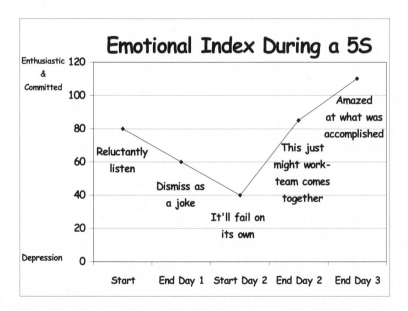

113

"Take a look at this, Fred. I keep this to remind myself that it'll get better after the first day. I know it, but they don't know it yet. Usually the team will bottom out sometime tomorrow morning."

"Wow, you've got this down to a science."

"It's human nature. Until they feel it all coming together and start getting excited to show off what they've accomplished at the report out session, they're frustrated. Right now they can't see the light at the end of the tunnel and don't even know where the tunnel leads. That's why I keep it to three days—so we can get through this period as quickly as possible."

"I certainly can relate to that. It looks like we have an impossible task."

"It'll get done, don't worry about that. And if I didn't know how good they'd feel at the end, do you think I'd put myself through this all the time? Just wait until it's over."

"I sure hope so. I guess I'll be here until nine o' clock tomorrow if I'm going to get through all my e-mails."

"No one said becoming World Class was easy."

"I'm convinced."

"Thanks for your help. See you tomorrow."

When Mike got back to his office, he reviewed his 5S checklist and realized he needed to send out the e-mail notification for the Wednesday afternoon report-out session. He selected twelve people from the various functions and requested that they attend the forty-minute meeting. He knew some would try to avoid the meeting or were unavailable, so he kept tabs on the responses so he could find substitutes if need be. His goal was to have a minimum of twelve people from across the company.

CHAPTER 12
MORNING KICK-OFF MEETING

DAY 2 (7:00 A.M.)

The team slowly filed into the training room. For the most part, they were not too happy about being there. Mike hated the second morning of an event and wanted to get through the meeting as quickly as possible so the team could get busy. But first he needed to make sure they all had a game plan. That was standard procedure for every morning and afternoon meeting. Mike always went over any issues and then went around the room and asked everyone what they were going to work on for the next few hours. He made sure they were focused.

"We've got a busy day ahead of us, so let's quickly go through what each of the sub-teams will be focusing on. Those of you doing the cleaning, start from the top and work your way down the machine."

"Do we have to do the walls also?" asked Christy.

"Yep, and the columns as well. Also, check with the sub-team that'll be focusing on containing the chips so you can develop counter measures. I'm sure the operators don't want to be cleaning them up forever."

"Hell no," said Joe. "If I have to clean the chips everyday, I'll never get any work done."

"That's why Anthony and Randall have such an important job. I suggest you all discuss a game plan. Christy, if you need any supplies and can't find them on the 5S cart, let me know."

"It'll take forever to clean the machine based on what we got done yesterday," responded Fred.

"Use the power washer. It'll make it a lot easier," responded Mike.

"Now you tell us," said Hubert, somewhat ticked off.

"I had to get it from the other building and I've already put it out there. Also, you should mop the floors before the end of the day. You'll need to have it clean to tape off all the areas."

Mike then looked at Josh. He was purposely focusing on the office folks to make sure they knew they had a key role and couldn't slack off. "Josh, do you have any questions?"

"If the operators don't like the racks they're using, can we build new ones?"

"Of course. What's the problem?" asked Mike.

"I was talking to Wendell and Joe and they mentioned they hate bending over to always get their tooling from the bottom shelves."

"So fix it. You're free to do anything. Also, try to get the racks closer to the point of use."

"What about my tool chest?" asked a very concerned Wendell.

"I checked out the list Harold gave me and we'll be buying the necessary tools. But I promised that you can keep the tool chest at the work center just in case. So mark off an area for the tool chest parking garage."

Wendell and Joe seemed satisfied with Mike's response.

Okay, what's next on the list, thought Mike. He glanced at the list of sub-teams on the flip chart and the next item was the set-up cart group with Jack and Wendell. He turned to question Jack and realized he wasn't in the room. "Does anyone know where Jack is?"

Josh spoke up. "He told me he had to get some things done before he could join us."

"Did he mention how long it would take?" asked Mike, trying his best to contain himself.

"Nope."

"Wendell, I'll find him after we wrap this up. In the meantime, help the cleaning team."

"Will do."

"Okay then, let's get going. Let's meet back here at eleven-thirty for lunch."

CHAPTER 13
WHERE'S JACK?

DAY 2 (7:15 A.M)

Everyone headed into the plant while Mike made a beeline for Jack's office. He didn't need a no-show in the middle of an event. Worse yet, if Jack can decide at any time that the event is not that important, Mike knew it would send a terrible signal to everyone else about the support Lean had from the rest of the company.

Mike found Jack in his office sitting at the computer. "Would you mind telling me why you didn't show up for the morning kick-off session?"

Jack spun around in his chair to face Mike. "Don't ask me, ask my boss."

"So Steve told you not to come?"

"Let's put it this way, Mike. We have a major marketing project review with corporate next week and Steve made it clear that I won't have any excuses if I'm not ready for it."

"And when did he say that?"

"When he stopped by my office this morning. I was in early to get some work done before the 5S event so I wouldn't get too far behind. Steve stopped by and asked me how I was doing and one thing led to another and he suggested I skip today's session. What the hell am I supposed to do if my boss tells me not to go?"

"Doesn't he understand that you'll be letting your teammates down and sending a terrible signal to the rest of the manufacturing group?"

"Mike, just between the two of us, I don't have anything against the 5S, but you know he couldn't care less."

"You're right. My beef's with him."

Mike headed to Steve's office but paused in the hall to call Peter first. Peter instructed Mike to let him know whenever he needed his support to keep the Lean transformation moving forward. Mike understood Peter's hectic travel schedule prevented him from participating in Lean events, but Peter agreed he would demand that his staff fully support Mike's efforts. Whether Peter understood exactly what this meant when Mike mentioned it during the interview process was still unclear, but he was about to find out now.

"Peter, sorry to bother you, but I need your help."

"I thought you were leading a 5S event this week," said Peter.

"I am. That's what it's about."

"What's the problem then?"

"I just wanted to give you a heads-up. Steve pulled Jack out of the event and I'm about to confront him on this."

"He must've had a good reason. Before you get too excited, why don't you find out what it's all about?"

"I already know. He wants Jack working on the presentation for the marketing project review meeting next week."

"I'll be at that meeting. There's a lot riding on it, you know."

"Well there's a lot riding on the Lean transformation as well."

"Jack is one of Steve's fair-haired boys. He relies on him a lot."

"Peter, let me be blunt. I really don't care about any of that. Steve knew about this meeting months ago and so did Jack. He's just using it as an excuse. There'll always be a reason to avoid participating in these events. And it's really important that we get all the key people to understand what this is all about. That's the only way it'll ever spread throughout the com-

pany. You know Lean only starts in manufacturing, and if it doesn't take hold everywhere
else, we'll fail."

"Okay, I've heard this speech before. Even I
have trouble fully understanding it."

"It's your support that's key. You remember
my telling you about 'no blink' situations?"

"Of course I do."

"Well, this is one of them. We can't blink at
all. We have to let Steve know he has no choice.
I'm going to his office now. I just wanted to let
you know that you may get a call from him and
when he does. . ."

"Don't worry, I won't blink. Jack will be at
the event."

"Thanks a lot. See you at the report-out session. You will be there, won't you?"

"I may not be able to take part in as many
events as you'd like, but the couple I did participate in convinced me that Lean's critical for our
future. That's why I'll do everything possible to
make the report-out sessions. It's the least I can
do. I'll be there."

"Great. Gotta go now."

Mike preferred that the President of this or
any company participate in most of the critical
Lean events, but he knew that often wasn't re-

ality. And if it wasn't reality, the next best thing was to have the president's full support in terms of resources, reward systems, and communications. Peter had fulfilled his promise by participating in a few kaizens and he really enjoyed it. Mike was sure Peter would do more if he didn't have to constantly meet with customers, the board, and Wall Street. As long as Peter made sure all the functional heads participated, the transformation would happen. Otherwise, without marketing, engineering, sales, accounting, human resources, and IT all pulling in the same direction, failure was inevitable. Mike demanded this support before signing on with Tricor, and Peter had backed him up as promised.

Mike walked into Steve's office as if on a mission. "Steve, I need Jack back with the rest of his team."

"Sorry, Mike, but I need him also. He's finishing up an important research project."

"You knew the ground rules before we started. This project isn't a new development."

"C'mon Mike, he's cleaning machines for crying out loud. He's one of my highest paid guys. I can't afford to have him out there..."

"Out where, in the shop with the manufacturing people? Is there something wrong with that? Are you guys above that?"

"I didn't mean it that way."

"Hell yes, you did. This isn't negotiable. I wanted to be reasonable with you, but you obviously don't care about what we're doing. I expect Jack out there within fifteen minutes."

"Or what?"

"Listen, Steve, you don't have any choice. I've already spoken with Peter."

Steve stood up and walked over to Mike. "You've gone too far this time. Just who the hell do you think you are?"

"Some day you'll thank me for this, like when we're kicking our competitor's butts and your job's a little easier because of what we did. I expect to see Jack in fifteen minutes."

Mike turned and left. He hated giving anyone an ultimatum, but didn't recall a Lean journey where it wasn't necessary at one point or another. Every company is the same. About ten percent of the workforce willingly supports the change effort, about eighty percent are fence sitters and will go either way depending on their experiences and their local leadership, and the last ten percent are trouble. This last group, the concrete heads, must be dealt with by either moving them to different positions or asking them to leave. And the higher up in the organization you have a concrete head, the greater the risk of derailing the transformation effort. Mike wasn't going to let Steve derail his efforts, no matter what he had to do.

CHAPTER 14
BACK AT THE WORK CENTER

DAY 2 (8:00-11:15 A.M.)

Mike spent most of the morning at the work center so that he was available for any questions. He also knew the cleaning had to get done first, so he spent the majority of his time helping the cleaning sub-team. He wanted to make sure no one cut any corners, which inevitably was the case when faced with such a big task, especially since the team had no idea what the definition of "clean" meant.

After about an hour, Mike saw Jack and Wendell flipping through the pages of a supply catalog. He walked over to see what they were doing, although he knew all too well. "What are you guys looking for?"

"We're looking for a set-up cart," responded Jack as he handed Mike a three-inch thick glossy catalog to look at.

"And you think you'll find what you need in

here?" said Mike.

"Sure, why not?" asked Wendell.

Mike knew it was time for another Lean lesson. "Let me explain the way Lean really works." The last thing we want is to become catalog engineers."

"Catalog engineers? What do you mean by that?" asked Jack.

"We're going to need customized cheap solutions to the challenges we're going to face every day as we reorganize the workplace. Typically the knee jerk reaction of any engineer is to pick up a catalog and see what we need to order. We call these people catalog engineers."

"So what's wrong with that?" pressed Jack.

"Just about everything. If we find something in a catalog, it won't be exactly what we need, will likely be too expensive, and will look too damn good."

"What the hell do looks have to do with this?" asked Wendell, totally confused.

"Let me explain," said Mike leaning up against a post while Jack and Wendell sat on a crate of parts. "It may not seem important to you now, and I'm sure it's totally counterintuitive, but we don't want anything to cost too much or look too good at this early stage. Right now we're just guessing what we need. We'll probably be fifty to seventy-five percent correct. No matter what you come up with for a set-up cart, it'll change two or three times over the next few months as the operators continually improve the process."

"So that's why you don't want to spend the money?" asked Jack.

"It's not just the money, Jack. Once you buy or make something that looks great, you have a lot of pride of ownership invested in the solution. The last thing you'll want to do is rip it apart when you realize that we need to redo it. That's when people typically dig in their heels. So if we make a cart out of materials in the plant with the knowledge that it'll likely be redone in the near term, we won't have a problem down the road."

"Do you think we could do it?" asked Wendell looking at Jack.

"I'm sure you both can. I was once in a world class facility in Eastern Europe. I was amazed as I walked around the plant and saw that just about everything was made of wood. And it wasn't even painted. My first reaction was the plant was a cash-starved facility in a depressed country..."

"Wasn't it?" interrupted Wendell.

"No way, I just didn't understand their strategy. They were truly World Class in every respect. The plant manager explained that they made a high tech product, cell phones, which have product life cycles of only about three months, after which time the plant had to be entirely reconfigured. They basically reorganized and modified everything once a quarter to accommodate the steady stream of new products. Since most everything was on wheels and made of wood, reconfiguring the plant was a lot easier, much more cost effective, and required far less downtime. They even started doing it with products that had much longer life cycles. The company's plants all over the world were just like this one."

"Boy, that's a totally different approach," said Jack.

"But doesn't it make sense?" asked Mike, hoping that some of what he just said sunk in.

"I guess so," said Wendell.

"C'mon guys, you're not buying it and I wouldn't expect you to just because I said so. But think about this. What makes us think that we can design anything that'll be the right solution today, as well as next year, and the year after that? We certainly can't do it with our products, can we Jack?"

"That's for sure. If we don't come out with new products every year, we'll get eaten alive."

"Well, it's no different in the plant. We have to continuously redesign our manufacturing processes. How we did it five or ten years ago might've been good at the time but it sure isn't today. So we need to acknowledge that survival requires continuous change, and therefore we want to spend as little as possible. If you need to get some wood at Home Depot, by all means put it on the supplies list. Also, make sure you buy some wheels so it's mobile. The rest you can make. It's all about brain power to get to the right solution. We don't want catalog engineers. How 'bout it?"

"Can we at least get some ideas from the catalog?" asked Wendell.

"Sure. But come up with a game plan and let's get it built today. The guys in the wood shop will help and if you need anything welded, just let me know. You'll need to get it done by this afternoon so we can put the tools on the cart, shadow board and label them, and test it out."

"You want it done today?" said Wendell incredulously.

"Sure do, so you guys better get going," said Mike as he walked away. He knew a tight deadline would force decisions and result in a good first pass of what was needed. No matter how long they took, it would change, so why bother with the waste of trying to design the perfect cart. Mike was a big believer of "plan, do, check, act" with an emphasis on keeping the planning stage to a minimum. Experience had taught him that there were ever decreasing returns on the additional time spent planning non-critical activities. The real gains were achieved by doing and redoing.

At the front of the work center, adjacent to the aisle, Josh was in an animated discussion with Joe and a couple of other team members. Mike walked over to see what was going on.

"So what's going on over here?" asked Mike.

"We're trying to figure out where to put all the parts once we bring the work back into the work center," said Josh. "We want to outline the location on the floor but there's just so much stuff."

"Really, show me what you have."

Josh, Fred, Joe, and Randall walked Mike over to the Red Tag area where the skids of parts were temporarily stored while the work center was being cleaned. Josh pointed to three skids jam packed with parts lying on top of each other. Mike was hoping this problem would be addressed by the team and welcomed this discussion.

"So what's the problem?" continued Mike.

"We want a separate location for incoming and outgoing parts," responded Josh.

"And?"

"Well, if we spread everything out, it'll take up so much room. . ." said Josh.

Joe interrupted. "That's why everything's piled on these skids."

"But doesn't that cause a problem, Joe?" asked Mike.

"What do you mean?" responded Joe, confused.

"If you need to find a part among that pile, doesn't it take a long time?"

"Never thought about that?"

"Mind if I ask you a few questions about the process then?"

"Go ahead."

"How do you know which job to work on next?"

Joe started to explain what he does, but Mike waved him off. "Let's go to the work center and show me." Mike knew it was one thing to hear about something but the best way to learn was by actually experiencing it. When they all got back to the work center, Mike continued, "Okay, show me as if you're going to work on your next job. How do you know what to work on?"

Joe walked up to the computer terminal and punched in some commands. "This tells me the next job I have to work on," said Joe, pointing to a job number on the computer screen.

"Okay, now show me what you'd do next."

"The job number tells me the six-digit part number that I have to machine. Now I need to get the material for the job. That's on the skids of parts in the Red Tag area."

"Okay then, let's go over there and find your next job."

The group followed Joe back over to the Red Tag area. Josh, Fred, and Randall were totally confused and annoyed.

"I'm goin' to get back to cleanin' up," said Randall as he started to walk away from the group.

When Mike noticed Randall walking away, he quickly caught up with him. "Randall, why don't you stay with us for a few minutes? I think you'll enjoy it."

"I ain't enjoyin' nothin' about this. We got a lot of cleanin' to do so I better be goin' back to help out."

"Not so fast. Do me a favor and stick with us for another ten minutes."

"Like I said before, as long as I'm getting paid, I'll do what you want."

They rejoined the group and Mike continued with his questioning. "Joe, show us how you find the material."

Fred looked at Josh as if to say what is Mike up to now. He knew Mike wouldn't waste their time, but he had no idea what Mike was doing.

Joe walked around the skids and started to rearrange the parts to find what he was looking for. That was no small task as the parts varied in size and shape and weighed as little as five or ten pounds and as much as two hundred and fifty pounds apiece. After a while Joe located what he was looking for.

"Now what do you want me to do?" asked Joe.

"Let's all gather around while I ask Joe a few questions. Fred, please keep track of his answers."

"What do you mean," asked Fred.

"You'll see," said Mike and he continued. He was obviously on a mission. "Joe, it took you about ten minutes to find that part. On average, how long does it usually take?"

"Sometimes it takes a lot longer and other times, if it's a familiar part, I can find it in half the time."

"What's a lot longer?"

"If it's a part I don't know, it can take up to a half-hour to sort through everything."

"And if it's an easy one, how long?"

"I'll find it in a few minutes, no sweat."

"Fred, keep track of the average time it takes to find a part."

"That's easy enough."

"Joe, how often do you get an easy one?"

"It depends."

"I know, but take a guess."

"Okay. Maybe half the time I recognize the part, but I still have to move stuff around."

"So then, how long should we use as an average time for an easy part?"

"Five minutes sounds good."

"Okay, now how about the other half of the time, the hard parts. How long should we use for them on average?"

Joe thought about it for awhile. "That's tough to say."

"Just give me your best guess. I don't expect you to be a hundred percent accurate and I really don't care about that. I just need a ballpark answer."

"Say twenty-five minutes then."

Everyone was starting to get impatient with

Mike. "Just a few more questions. How many jobs do you do in a shift?"

"You know we have very short runs here, just a few pieces at a time. It's not like I set-up my machine and it runs for hours."

"I know. So how many jobs do you do?"

"About four jobs a day."

"You mean a shift, don't you?"

"Yep."

"How long are your set-ups?"

"Fifty-six minutes. You showed that yesterday."

"Does the set-up time include finding the parts?"

"Sure does."

"So what's the average Fred?"

"Fifteen minutes."

"So that means your set-ups are, on average, fifteen minutes to find the part and forty-one minutes to actually set the machine up. And if you do four jobs a day you spend about half the day in set-ups."

"That's about right."

"And one hour a day, I mean a shift, is spent looking for parts. This work center usually runs two shifts, doesn't it?"

"Sure does."

"Just a couple more questions. How many work centers do we have in the machine shop?"

"I think it's forty," volunteered Fred.

"And do most of them run two shifts?"

"About half of them do."

"And do they store parts in pretty much the same fashion?"

"Sure do," said Joe. "We've always done it that way."

"Great, we have all the information we need now. Fred, I'd like you to calculate how much time we spend a year in the machine shop looking for parts. Then I'd like this group to figure out how we can reduce the time by at least fifty percent, because it's waste and the customer doesn't pay us for it."

"You want us to do that today?" asked Josh, reeling from the overflow of information.

"Sure do. I don't know how you'll lay out the work center if you don't know how you'll be storing the parts. If you have any questions I'll be around."

Mike left the group to check up on everyone else. While he didn't have the exact answer to the challenge he had just given the team, he knew the company couldn't afford to spend so much time on non-value-added work. He felt he needed to make the waste visible and the team would do the rest. He knew they were never given the opportunity to eliminate waste.

Meanwhile, Fred, Joe, Randall, and Josh were huddled in a corner trying to recover from Mike's inquisition.

"Fred, what's it costing us to look for parts?" asked Josh.

"Give me a few minutes to figure it out. Why don't you three start thinking about how we can do it differently?"

After about ten minutes, Fred gathered the group to review his calculations. He shared his spreadsheet with them, which in this case was the back of a piece of cardboard.

Waste Looking for Parts

Tricor Machine Shop

♦ extra minutes per job—15 minutes

♦ # of jobs per shift—4 jobs

♦ # of shifts per day—2 shifts

♦ # of work centers—40 machines

♦ # of work centers operating on two shifts—20

♦ # of workdays per year—250 days

♦ potential Muda looking for parts = 15,000 hours/year x $20/hour = $300,000/yr.

"That's unbelievable," said Joe.

"Never would've thought about it," said Randall.

"Either would I, and I'm the CFO," said Fred. I guess Mike's point is that it really doesn't matter what the exact numbers are. It's a lot of money and we should come up with a better way of doing it."

"I think we have an answer," said Joe.

"Already?" said Fred anxiously.

"Yeah, Josh came up with a great idea while you were doing the calculations."

They all discussed Josh's idea, fine tuned it, and agreed it would work. They couldn't wait to share it with the rest of the group when they got back together in the Training Room. They especially couldn't wait to see Mike's reaction.

Meanwhile, Mike was looking at the list of supplies on the flip chart he had placed in the work area. A number of items had been listed, including wheels, plywood, and cleaning supplies. It was time to send a couple of team members on a shopping trip.

Mike called everyone to gather around the flip chart.

"I need a couple of volunteers to head to Home Depot."

Joe immediately spoke up. "Josh knows what we need—he should go."

Mike immediately agreed. He knew Joe wanted to have some fun with Josh. "Anyone else want to go?"

"I guess I'll help out," volunteered Jack. "I need to get some pegboard and hooks for the set-up cart."

They grabbed the list from the flip chart and

headed out, vests and all.

The others went back to their assignments except for Fred. He wanted a word with Mike.

"I can't believe how much time we waste looking for parts."

"I thought you'd learn something from pushing those numbers."

"It's amazing."

"Do you think you'd ever understand the operation well enough to discover these opportunities from behind a desk?"

"No way we could understand these nuances."

"You betcha. How about your cost accounting reports—do they point out this waste?"

"You know the answer to that Mike. You don't need to rub my nose in it."

"Sorry about that. One last thing. Even if we did achieve standard performance, whatever that might be, would you have any idea how much waste was incurred?"

"Nope."

"And yet everyone would feel relieved because we hit standard. I'm telling you Fred, our standard costs are meaningless. You're staff needs to learn how to identify waste, quantify it, and help the kaizen teams eliminate it. That's the only way we'll be able to compete globally."

"I'm getting a much better understanding of this stuff now. I can see how you need to be out in the shop and really pay attention."

"Good! Do me a favor. I have some things to work on upstairs to get ready for the group. Please make sure everyone comes back up at eleven-fifteen. I want to go over some things before lunch."

"Will do."

CHAPTER 15
PRE-LUNCH STATUS REPORT

DAY 2 (11:15-11:30 A.M.)

Everyone from the team was back in the Training Room with the exception of Josh and Jack who hadn't returned from the supplies run yet. Mike knew it was critical to check on the progress of each of the sub-teams and make sure they had a plan of attack for the afternoon. Mike used this technique at every break. It was the only way to get through an event and stay on track.

"Let's go through the teams one by one to see if you have any questions and then let's discuss where you think you'll be by the end of today. Fred, how's your group doing with cleaning the area?"

"It looks like Fred's been busy, and he hasn't just been adding numbers," heckled Joe.

"Okay, guys, have your fun, but you'll be thanking me tomorrow afternoon."

"C'mon, let Fred answer the question. We've still got a lot to do." said Christy.

"Go ahead, Fred. How's your group doing?"

"We've done quite a bit. We found out that we don't need the filing cabinet and that the storage cabinet was filled with junk. We still have a fair amount of cleaning to do on the machine though. Otherwise we're in decent shape. Everyone's been a big help."

"Will you be done by the end of the day?"

"It'll be close."

"You'll need to finish so we can mop down the floor and let it dry over night."

"Do we really need to do that?" asked Christy.

"Yep. We'll be taping off the areas tomorrow and we need a clean floor to do that."

"Your team will have to develop a 5S checklist."

"What's that?" asked Hubert.

"After going through such an extensive cleaning of the work center, we want to make sure it stays that way. So your team needs to develop a cleaning schedule that the operators can follow."

"No way we're doing that every day," protested Wendell.

"Don't worry. You won't need to do that every day. The checklist will divide all the activities into smaller increments and you'll do a little each day. Let me show you an example from another work center."

4th S - Schedule
5S Activities Check List
Work Center 234

Perform Daily	Perform On: (as noted)	Initial & Date When Completed	Activity
x			Clean out chips from inside machine areas
x			Sweep floor
x			Blow off chips (table and machine)
x			Remove all unnecessary items from the machine (rags, gloves, clamps, tools etc)
x			Replace tools (when dull, broken, etc.)
x			Make sure everything is in its place before leaving the area (clamps, tools, etc)
	Monday		Wipe down tool cart
	Tuesday		Wipe down tool box
	Wednesday		Wipe down tool rack
	Thursday		Mop Floor
	Friday		Wipe down machine

"Fred and Wendell, can you give me a draft of a cleaning schedule by the end of the day? Once you finalize it, I'll laminate it and you'll need to hang it in the work center."

Fred looked across the room to see if Wendell was in agreement. Wendell was not entirely buying into the process, but reluctantly agreed to work on it with Fred.

"Thanks, Wendell. One last thing. Can your sub-team work late today? We haven't started labeling anything and that'll take a long time."

Mike didn't get any takers so he moved on. He'd come back to this a little later.

"Anthony and Randall, how are you doing with chip containment?"

"We've agreed on some designs for the chip guards," responded Anthony.

"Have both operators seen them?"

"Yep. We've changed the design based on their input."

"Have you tested it out yet?"

"How can we do that, we haven't made them yet?"

"Make them out of cardboard and see if the operators can still comfortably work at the machine."

"Good idea," said Wendell.

"Who's going to make the guards?"

"The guys in sheet metal have agreed to help," said Anthony

"Great. If you guys finish early, help the cleaning crew or start labeling."

"Wendell, how's the set-up cart going?"

"Jack's getting what we need at Home Depot right now. We've got a plan."

"Good. You'll need to get it done quickly. Do you need any help?"

"We'll let you know if we do."

"How's the last team doing, tooling?"

Harold was anxious to respond. "We got all the new tools already, including power tools where it makes sense. We're spray painting them the same color so it'll be easy to know which work center they belong to. We saw that in one of your slides yesterday."

"Good. What else?"

"We're making some shelves to mount tools right on the machine so Joe and Wendell don't have to keep walking back and forth to the work-bench."

"I'm sure they'll appreciate that."

"We do," bellowed Wendell. "It gets tiring out there."

"And we're making new racks so that some of the tooling is moved to chest height to avoid the constant bending that Joe told us he hates."

"Do you guys have a game plan for this afternoon?"

"Yeah, we're working with Harold to eliminate trips to the tool crib by having some visual signals. We haven't figured it all out but we're close."

"Sounds great."

Just then Jack and Josh burst into the room.

"Glad you two could join us," teased Mike.

"So how did it go?" asked Joe, grinning from ear to ear in anticipation.

"You know," said Josh

"How could he know?" asked Christy. "He didn't go with you guys."

"Why don't you tell her?" needled Joe.

"Okay already. Jack and I were going up and down the aisles and every once in awhile some-one would come up to us and ask for directions or advice on how to fix something."

"Boy, I bet you guys were a lot of help," joked Harold.

"Yeah, did you give them some tips for marketing plans?" shouted Paul.

"So how long did it take before you guys figured it out?" asked Joe.

"After about the fourth customer came up to us," said Josh, somewhat embarrassed.

"Figure what out?" pressed Christy.

"That we were wearing orange vests and looked like we worked there," said Jack.

"I told you," said Joe. "It happens all the time. You don't even realize you have the vest on after a while."

The group had a lot of fun needling the two guys from the office. Mike had some more topics to cover before lunch, so he cut in. "A small group of us were working on a waste elimination problem this morning and I wanted to share it with everyone." Mike asked Fred to explain how much time and money was spent looking for parts. The team was amazed by the annual cost.

"Thanks, Fred. "I understand you guys came up with a better way of doing it."

"Sure did," said Randall showing the first

signs of life. "It's a really neat idea. It was Josh's idea so he should be tellin' you about it."

"Go ahead and tell them Randall, that's okay with me," said Josh, encouraging Randall to continue.

"Okay. Josh said we could save about ninety percent of the lookin' time if we just sorted the parts on the floor by the last digit of the part number. This way when we need to find a part we just look up the part number and if it ends in a seven it will be in the group marked seven. We're going to label the floor that way. Spots for zero to nine."

"That's a really neat and easy way to do it," said Mike. "What do the operators think?"

"We think it'll work," said Joe

"Great. If it works as well as expected, then it's something we should do at the other work centers where the same challenges exist. So Paul, don't forget that once this event is over. I have one more thing before we get lunch. Tomorrow at two o'clock we'll be having our report-out session. I've invited about twelve people to attend and they'll want to know what we've been doing for these three days."

"Who's invited?" asked Jack.

"Folks from every department, including a number of department managers."

"And what happens?" asked Christy.

"The way it works is I'll open up the meeting and explain what a 5S is, I'll introduce everyone and then I'll turn it over to all of you."

"What are we supposed to do?" asked Anthony.

"The team will spend a few minutes in this room explaining what areas of waste we were working on and then take everyone out to the work center to show them what we've done. I'll show the before pictures and you'll be showing them the changes."

"How long is the report-out session?" asked Hubert.

"About forty minutes. Fifteen minutes up here, about twenty minutes in the work area, and then we'll come back here for questions and answers. So we better be ready. And by the way, Peter will be back for the meeting. He loves to see the changes and hear what all of you have to say about this."

"What do you mean 'all of us'?" asked Randall.

"I'd like everyone to take part in the report-out session, but it's up to you. No one will be forced to do anything. Okay, now let's get lunch. We'll meet back here at three fifteen."

"Even if we're going to stay late today?"

153

"Yeah, we always need to do a wrap-up to see where we are, see if we need to make a supply run, and plan out the next day."

Mike always made sure the team knew about the report-out session on Tuesday to place a little bit of added pressure on the team to finish up their projects. The fact that the president, Peter, would be attending was the extra push everyone needed. If nothing else, it created a sense of urgency that usually motivated the majority of team members to stay late on Tuesday.

While everyone was eating, Mike updated the flip chart to indicate what each sub-team would be working on during the afternoon. He would make sure to post it in the work area so that everyone would stay focused on their assignments.

CHAPTER 16
AFTERNOON WORK SESSION

DAY 2 (12:15-3:15 P.M.)

During the afternoon, everyone worked feverishly on their projects. At this point, everyone usually is pretty focused; they know what has to be done, know when the deadline is, and realize they better all pull together or the report-out session will be a disaster. It's also a time when the task seems somewhat impossible as a lot has to be done in the next twenty-four hours. Mike constantly coached the teams and helped them set expectations for what would be finished by the report-out session. He knew that by the second afternoon, it was best to concentrate on fewer but more important items, rather than completing the entire list. There would be time for all the other items after the event was finished.

The one item that had to be completed during the event was the clean-up of the entire work center. There would never be a better opportunity to complete this task than during the event.

While Mike was assisting the teams, he heard his name being paged by Joan Russell, the master production scheduler for the facility. Her office was nearby and he headed off to see her.

"Joan, what's up?" he asked as he walked into her office.

"Mike, we could really use Work Center 111 tomorrow. We got a bunch of orders that need to be addressed as soon as possible."

"You know we're in the middle of a 5S event and we have the machine torn apart. There's no way we can do anything until after the event is over."

"I thought the customer always comes first. You've always said that. If we don't produce those parts we'll be in trouble."

"C'mon Joan, don't give me that crap. Yeah, the customer comes first and we all know that; that's why we put these events into the master schedule. I didn't schedule this at the last minute. You're supposed to have a contingency plan to cover us for these three days, either by building ahead or lining up an operator on another work center, or lining up an outsourcing option. Don't tell me you haven't done that."

"I've been so busy I didn't get to it. I thought we were covered."

"Well, we better think of an alternative pretty

fast, because there's no way we could get the machine operational now anyway. It's completely torn apart. We discovered some hydraulic lines that need to be replaced and maintenance will need a day after the event."

"You mean we won't be getting the machine back until Thursday night?"

"That's right. And believe me, you're lucky at that. If we didn't get in there and fix some of the things we found, you would've lost that machine for a couple of weeks, and most likely when we needed it the most. Isn't it funny, we figure a way to work around a machine when it unexpectedly breaks down, but we can't plan for it to be out of service. That's another paradigm we have to change."

"C'mon Mike, I'm just trying to do my job and get assembly the parts they need on time. Are you going to rake me over the coals for that?"

"Hey, I'm sorry. Let me see if I can get industrial engineering to help offload the parts."

"Thanks."

"And by the way, Joan, plan on the machine being out of service until Monday."

"Monday, you gotta be kidding. Why?"

"Because the team will likely want to paint the machine and they'll need to do that over the weekend."

"IE better bail me out of this mess."

"If they can't, let me know. I don't want any mud slinging at Lean because the machine's out of service. I really need you to come through for me."

"I'll do the best I can."

"I know you will. Thanks"

Mike went back to the Training Room to review the list of brainstorming ideas and assess the team's progress. He updated the chart as best he could and would get the team's help at the three-fifteen meeting.

Brainstorming Ideas - Work Center 111				
Improvement Activity	**Category**	**Votes**	**Team Members**	**Status**
1. Clean out all cabinets 4. Sort Items and Red Tag 6. Provide a place for cleaning supplies 7. Clean walls 32. Clean entire area 47. Organize file cabinet 48. Remove junk on top of machine	Cleaning	9	Fred Christy Mike Hubert	Complete Complete Complete Complete Complete Complete
2. Return tools to tool crib 13. Remove fixtures belonging to other work centers 19. Minimize trips to the tool crib 20. Set up tooling kanban 22. Need two tooling racks, one mounted on machine 24. Eliminate tool chests 29. Mark and label all tools 30. Group tooling by common use on top cabinet in holders 33. Minimize trips to tool crib 38. Re-evaluate all tools kept at machine and relocate to point of use 49. Add power tools	Tooling	9	Josh Joe Harrold Paul	Complete In Process Wednesday In Process Complete
3. Make set-up cart 23. Build set-up cart on wheels 37. Make set-up tools mobile	Set-up Cart	7	Jack Wendell	In Process In Process In Process
5. Chips everywhere-clean up 26. Build chip guards 40. Cover pockets at base of machine 44. Provide retractable barrier to collect/redirect chips	Confine Chips	6	Anthony Randall	Complete In Process Complete In Process
8. Repaint machine a light color				TBD
10. Mark staging areas 21. Standardize materail handling equipment 27. Identify finsihed goods in work center 31. Location of fixture pallets - color coded or numbered by machine	Material Handling	6		Wednesday
9. Make coolant collection trays 42. Make troughs for way lube	Control Fluids	6		In Process Complete
12. Routings should reference tooling locations				
14. Provide a hanger for mounting prints 15. Mount computer on column 16. Provide set-up visuals 17. Make bulletin board 41. Post set-up procedures 46. Provide a convenient holder for drawings 25. Provide fixture pictures on set-up sheets	Information	5		In Process Complete
11. Mount retractable hose reel near point of use 45. Remove air line that is a tripping hazard		2		Complete Complete
34. New ball screw for machine (it's in house) 18. Prepare TPM schedule 35. Get dedicated crane 36. Get new floor mat for operator 39. Provide a home for lifting straps and magnet 43. Make a shim box and organize 28. Eliminate clocking on and off jobs - it's waste		2 1 1 1 1		After Event Complete Wednesday Wednesday

CHAPTER 17

AFTERNOON MEETING

DAY 2 (3:15 P.M.)

Once again, the group gathered in the Training Room. They were getting used to the drill by now and were more comfortable with each passing meeting. It helped that they all were focused on a mission and welcomed Mike's help, at least most of them did.

"Before we update the list, does anyone have any questions?"

"I do," said Joe. "Are we going to paint the machine?"

"What did the team decide?"

"We can't agree on it."

"What do you want to do, Joe?"

"If I'm going to work there, then I want it painted. You said everything should be a light color so we can spot the leaks. Can't do that when it's dark blue."

"What do you want to do, Paul?" asked Mike, as he noticed Paul was obviously not in agreement with Joe.

"We don't have the time to get it ready to be painted. And besides, I heard we got some orders yesterday and need to get the machine back into production. I don't think we should do it."

"What do you think, Anthony? You're the one who has to take care of the machine."

"It was great when we painted the machine in the last work center. It really made my job easier. I think we should do it."

"Anyone else want to add anything to the discussion?"

Wendell spoke up. "If we paint it, we have to wait until the weekend."

"Why's that?" asked Fred.

"Because of the paint fumes, we have to do it when the building's empty," responded Mike. He wasn't going to make the same mistake as last time. During the first machine shop 5S, Mike asked a couple of painters to paint the machine on the night shift the day the event ended. He took a lot of heat from the entire plant the next day, not to mention what Barb in HR had to say.

Paul saw an opening to support his position and jumped right in. "That means we'd have to wait until the weekend and lose two more days of production. I don't see how we can do it. I'm getting beat up to get parts and I can't do it if I don't have the machine."

"Okay, I've heard what some of you think. Let's take a vote; you're the ones that'll have to live with it." Mike handed out his trusty sticky notes again. "Just write down paint or don't paint, fold it over, and I'll come around and pick them up."

Mike handed the pile of sticky notes to Christy and asked her to read off the votes as he kept a tally on the flip chart.

"Looks like the team voted to paint the machine by a vote of eight to three."

"But what about the parts we need?" objected Paul.

"You're right Paul; we definitely have to take care of our customers. This is not a win/lose proposition. So here's an idea for the team to consider. What if we paint the machine Friday night? Could we run parts by Sunday?"

"I don't know much about painting, but I think if we use an accelerator it'll be dry in time," responded Anthony.

"Great, can you talk to the painters and verify that?"

163

"Sure will."

"Joe and Wendell..."

"Ah, c'mon Mike, don't go there," said Joe, shaking his head."

"What do you think I'm gonna say?"

"You're going to ask us to work on Sunday."

"Bingo! I gotta ask that. But let me throw out this idea before you answer."

"Gee, I can't wait," said Wendell. "It better be good."

"Since the machine will be out of commission on Friday waiting to be painted, how about if you two take Friday off and come in on Sunday?"

"Do we have to take Friday off?" asked Joe.

"No, you know that there's plenty of other work for both of you to do. It's entirely up to you."

"I like the idea," said Wendell. "I've got a bunch of stuff I gotta get done this weekend and Friday off would be great. "I'll come in on Sunday."

"Thanks."

"Hell, if Wendell's coming in, so will I. And

we'll get OT, won't we?"

"How about if we work something out with comp time?"

"That'll be okay," said Joe.

"Great. We should be in decent shape by Monday. Joan's working on offloading some of the parts and you two will take care of the rest of them."

"Do we really need to do all of this?" asked Randall. "Doesn't it ever end?"

"Randall, you're always complaining about not getting parts on time from the machine shop. Sometimes it's because the machine's out of service, so this is going to help you in the long run."

"So what, he'll just find something else to complain about," said Hubert.

"Ain't that the truth," agreed Wendell.

"Okay, enough," said Mike. "Let me explain how the Japanese treat their equipment. I was on a study mission in Japan and we were walking out by the receiving dock when my host stopped to point out a new piece of equipment being delivered to their plant. He turned toward me and said that was the worst condition that equipment would ever be in. Can you imagine that?"

"I'm not sure I understand," said Jack.

"What he meant was that the folks in the plant constantly modify the equipment to make it easier to maintain, easier to keep it clean, and easier to operate. That's the culture of a World Class company. The equipment improves as they understand it better, whereas we tend to operate the equipment until it breaks down."

"I've had it with all these Japanese stories," said Randall, getting up to leave.

"Hold on Randall. What exactly is bothering you?" said Mike, trying to calm him down.

"You keep talkin' about the Japanese. If they're so good, how come their economy stinks? My father taught me to buy American. I can't take this Japanese stuff with the funny words anymore. We're in America in case you haven't figured that out yet."

"Randall, most everything the Japanese learned fifty years ago came from American consultants."

"So why do you keep usin' them as an example?"

"Because they're the best at it. No one in our country listened to the consultants, so they helped the Japanese. Heck, you can trace some of the beginnings of Lean back to Henry Ford."

"No kiddin'."

"It's true. But the difference is some Japanese companies listened to everything the consultants said and then continually added new techniques. They've been doing this for fifty years. Some leading American companies started Lean about fifteen years ago, but for the most part, Lean just started to take off in this country in the last decade."

Fred was intrigued by the conversation and picked up on Randall's earlier comment. "So why's the Japanese economy been stagnant for so long if they have some of the best manufacturing companies in the world?"

"They have a lot of other problems they need to overcome."

"Like what?" asked Jack.

"Their banking system for one. Unlike our system, they don't let companies that are doing poorly go bankrupt. It's very different from ours. Also, the political system is different. So, who knows where Japan would be if they didn't have great manufacturing companies."

"We have good companies also," insisted Randall.

"We do, but no one, either in America or anywhere else, is as good as Toyota. And Lean is really the Toyota Production System as I explained yesterday."

"What's so good about Toyota?" asked Josh.

"Toyota has the best quality, the lowest costs, the greatest market share growth, and the largest profit of any automotive company in the world. So that's why everyone's trying to copy their methods. You may not like it, but if we want to get better, we have to use the best techniques, whether they're from Japan or anywhere else. So let's not get hung up by where the tools or methods come from and instead focus on how we can put them to good use."

Mike thought he had spent enough time on this. The good news was Randall didn't walk out; he stood at the back of the room and kept listening. Mike reached for a packet of sticky notes and asked Christy to take one and pass the packet around the room.

"What's this for?" asked Harold as he peeled off his sticky note.

"We need to vote for two team captains," replied Mike.

"Team captains? Why do we need team captains?" asked Jack. "We're almost done."

"A lot will be accomplished this week, but not everything on the list will be completed. After the event, the team's charged with closing out all the open items."

"When do we do that?" wondered Wendell.

"There's a sunset provision for each event. I'd like to have everything wrapped up within sixty days. The captains are responsible for keeping the team focused once the event is over. They have to make sure the team meets briefly each week and gets together as necessary to complete the open item list. Their job is to keep the process moving forward. So write down two names, fold the sticky note in half, and I'll come around and collect them in a couple of minutes."

The room went silent as everyone thought about the task at hand. Randall walked over to his seat and picked up the sticky note that was left at his empty seat. They were all looking around and silently assessing who would be a good leader. Mike always guessed who would be selected and was amazed that the teams' selections were on target ninety-nine percent of the time. Everyone always took this part seriously. A few minutes passed and Mike collected the sticky notes.

"Just a couple more things. Does anyone need any more supplies? This is our last chance."

Mike listed the items as they were called out and let the team know he would pick up everything that evening.

"Wendell, have you completed the 5S cleaning schedule?"

Wendell got up and handed Mike a schedule. "Hope this works."

Mike studied the schedule. "Looks good. I'll

type it up tonight and laminate it so you can hang it up tomorrow."

"Mike, aren't you going to tell us who the captains are?" asked Christy, never satisfied to let anything pass.

"Yeah, just give me a few minutes to go through the votes. In the meantime, would you all please 5S this room."

Mike sat down and tallied the votes while the team straightened out the room. Josh and Joe captured the most votes by a wide margin. Mike was somewhat surprised that Josh was elected, but then again Josh had worked extremely hard and had come up with some really novel ideas that everyone liked. He obviously won the respect of his teammates.

"So, who is it?" asked Christy one more time.

"Josh and Joe."

"Way to go, Josh," said Jack cynically.

"Man, I can't believe this," said Josh as he wondered where he would get the time to devote to the team.

"One last thing," Mike called out to the group as they were starting to leave. "If anyone wants to work late tonight, please do. We have a lot to finish for the report-out session tomorrow and anything else we can do today would be a huge help."

Five team members decided to stay: Josh, Fred, Joe, Harold, and Wendell. Mike was encouraged as the group was starting to gel. Mike spent about half an hour organizing his materials and then went to the work center. He always inspected the work center the evening before the report-out session for a couple of reasons. First, he conducted a final Red Tag inspection of the area, noting those items the team might have overlooked. Secondly, he wanted to come up with a game plan for the report-out session. Mike had to assess what could be accomplished by the Wednesday meeting and limit the final day's work to just those items. He made some notes for the morning meeting and then walked over to have a word with Fred.

"Thanks for staying late today."

"We have a hell of a lot to do by tomorrow afternoon and I want to make sure my end of the bargain's complete."

"The team will appreciate that. Having you out here will make a difference in more ways than just cleaning."

"No way I won't be ready for the report-out session. I've learned a lot about this machine, climbing over it for two days now. I've also gotten to know the other guys more in two days than all the time I've been at the company. It's worth it, despite the fact that I'm filthy and my back's killing me."

"Glad to hear that," said Mike while putting

his arm on Fred's shoulder.

"Glad to hear my back's killing me?"

"I didn't mean that. I'm glad you think it's worth it."

Mike turned and walked over to Josh and Wendell who were busy building the set-up cart. "Josh, I thought you were on the tooling sub-team?"

"I am. We're in good shape, so I thought I'd help Wendell out with the cart."

"Where are the tooling racks?"

"We had some help cutting them down and we made a couple of smaller racks to store the fixtures at the right height. The racks are in the paint booth now. Wanted to get that done early so they'd be dry by tomorrow morning and we can set them up and label them."

"So what are you doing over there?" asked Mike, pointing to a pile of tools lying on the floor.

Josh walked over to a three by three foot piece of cardboard that was leaning against a wall and turned it over to show Mike. "We experimented laying out the tools in different configurations until Joe and Wendell were satisfied. Then we shadowed them with black magic marker. Now we're going to do the real thing with the pegboard and then attach the pegboard to the cart. It's kind of cool."

"What do you think, Wendell?"

"It's just like the pictures you showed us, Mike."

"Yeah, but what I'm really asking is do you think it'll work? I could care less if it's like a picture; will it work for you?"

"Yeah. Me and Joe like it."

"Good. If you need to change anything, just do it."

"So, what's the spray paint for, Josh?"

"I'm spreading out all the tools and then I'll paint some stripes on them. Harold's already done this to the stuff he bought, so we need to be consistent. After all this work, we don't want any of the tools finding their way to another work center. This way we can identify them."

"Josh, if I didn't know better, I'd think you were actually having some fun out here."

"You should have seen him designing the cart," said Wendell. "The guys got some talent."

"Reminds me of when I was a kid and competed in the soap box derby. That's why I became an engineer. I love making stuff."

"I'll remember that for when we need volunteers for another kaizen event."

Fred walked over to join the group. "Better not let Randy hear this conversation."

"I know what you mean," said Josh. "I don't think he'll be too happy if I need to spend more time on this after the event's over."

"I'll talk to him," said Fred, dreading the thought.

CHAPTER 18
MORNING MEETING

DAY 3 (7:00 A.M.)

The morning meeting started off like every other meeting during the last two days. Mike went through each sub-team's open item list and asked for an assessment of where they would be by lunchtime. The tone was a little different this time. Everyone was in a hurry to finish the meeting and get out to the work center so they could get going. They were under the gun and knew it. Day three was always intense.

"What about the report-out session?" asked Harold.

"It'll start at two o'clock. We need some volunteers to explain what's been going on. How about you, Wendell? Would you like to talk about the set-up cart? You've done some really neat stuff."

"I guess so, but what do I say?"

"Just explain why you built the cart, why you spray-painted the tools, and how you think this will help you."

"That's easy enough."

"Who else?"

"How about Josh?" offered up Wendell. "He came up with a great idea to find parts. He should explain that."

"Josh, would that be okay?"

"Not a problem."

"Great. Who else? How about someone from the team that built the new racks and set up the tooling kanban?" Mike looked around the room and it was as if everyone were looking for cover. This was a typical response and he knew he had to coax them along. And it never failed, once they started talking during the report-out session, it was difficult to get them to stop. They were proud of what they did and enjoyed sharing it. That's why Mike felt he needed to encourage them to participate. "Harold, Paul, or Joe, how about it?"

Harold half heartedly raised his hand. "I guess I can do that."

Mike wrote Harrold's name on the flip chart next to the others. "What else?" Mike scanned all of the flip charts lining the room. "How about all the guards that were built to make the cleaning so much easier? Anthony or Randall, how about it?"

Randall just sat there and didn't acknowledge Mike's comments.

"Ah, what the hell, I'll do it," said Anthony.

"We also need to review the 'Just the Facts' data."

Fred raised his hand. "I'll take care of that."

"I was expecting that. Some of the data will have to wait until the machine's back up, but we need to let everyone know this is all about improving, not just cleaning the machine."

"I'll make sure they understand that."

"Great. It'll be credible coming from you."

"One last thing. Would someone go through the cleaning schedule? It's important that everyone know how we plan to maintain the work center."

"I can do that," volunteered Christy. "After all the work I did cleaning that machine, Joe and Wendell better take care of it!"

"Give 'em hell, Christy," shouted Jack. Everyone had a good laugh.

"Have we missed anything? Does anyone else want to say anything to the group?" There was a brief silence after which Mike continued with the next item. "I'm handing out a few sheets of paper. The first two sheets are the *5S Manufacturing Area Guidelines*. The next sheet in your packet is the *5S Master Scoring Criteria*, and the last sheet is the *5S Audit Score Sheet*. I want you to see what we expect."

177

5S Manufacturing Area Guidelines

Sort Location	Evaluation Criteria
All	All unnecessary items (equipment, work-in-process, raw material, tools, fixtures, gauges, partitions, files) are removed from the work area.
Bulletin Boards/ Production Boards	All displayed notices are necessary. Production board information is current.
Documents	Only documents which will be used today are in the work areas.
Floors/ Aisles	Only process related items are on the floor. Aisles are not blocked. There is easy access to all emergency equipment, electrical panels, and exits.
Straighten Location	Evaluation Criteria
All	All equipment, partitions, furniture, and storage cabinets are arranged neatly and conveniently.
Bulletin boards/ Production boards	All notices are displayed in a straight and neat manner. All notices hang within the frame of the board. No torn or soiled notices are displayed.
Documents	Documents and binders which will be used today are stored in a neat and orderly fashion. Document binders are clearly labeled as to content and responsibility for control and revision.
Equipment	Equipment controls are correctly labeled and critical points for daily maintenance checks are clearly marked. Equipment check sheets are up-to-date, clean, and neatly displayed.
Floors/ Aisles	Aisles are clearly marked and there is no storage in the aisles or on the markings. Objects are always placed at right angles to the aisle lines. No raw material, work-in-process, finished goods, tools, or gauges are stored directly on floor. No items block electrical cabinets, fire extinguishers, or emergency exits.
Shelves	Shelves are marked so it is clear where things are stored and where they should be returned. All shelves are in good repair and properly supported.
Storage	Nothing is stored on top of equipment or cabinets. Storage of boxes, totes, and containers is always neat and at right angles to the aisles and parallel to each other. Cleaning supplies are stored in an identified location, in a neat manner, and are readily available when needed.
Tools, Fixtures, & Gauges	Equipment must be arranged and stored so that it is easily accessible to the operator, depending on its use to monitor quality or for tool changes. The storage location must also keep the tools, fixtures, and gauges clean and protected from damage.
Walls	Anything hung on the walls (bulletin boards, drawings, process sheets, pictures etc.) is hung at the same distance from the ceiling. Everything is displayed in a frame or holder.

5S Manufacturing Area Guidelines

Sweep Location	Evaluation Criteria
All	All equipment, tools, fixtures, gauges, partitions, table tops, furniture, and file cabinets are kept clean. Work surfaces and glass are kept clean and polished.
Floors/Aisles	Floors are clean and free of dirt.
Tools, Fixtures, & Gauges	Tools, fixtures & gauges are clean and free of residual magnetism. Critical areas are protected to prevent damage.
Schedule Location	Evaluation Criteria
All	There is evidence that a schedule exists to maintain all Sort, Straighten, and Sweep criteria. Cleaning methods and frequencies are identified.
Sustain Location	Evaluation Criteria
All	There is evidence that people are committed and becoming disciplined to continuously keeping 5S at highest possible levels. 5S audits are performed regularly with results posted.

5S Master Scoring

Sort Points	Description
5	Unneeded items have been completely disposed of.
4	All unneeded items are in Red Tag parking lot (awaiting disposition).
3	It is easy to distinguish between needed and unneeded items.
2	It is difficult to distinguish between needed and unneeded items.
1	Needed and unneeded items are mixed together. It is not possible to determine the difference between needed and unneeded items.

Straighten Points	Description
5	All tools and gauges are identified and in their proper location. Supplies and raw material areas are clearly marked for part number and quantity per location.
4	Color coding, outlining, or other methods are used to facilitate placement of tools, gauges, supplies, and materials. Quantity per location not marked.
3	Location and item indicators are used for tools, gauges, supplies, and raw materials. Aisles are clearly marked. Some items may be out of place.
2	It is difficult to distinguish what goes where and in what quantities. Some items and locations may be marked.
1	It is not possible to determine what goes where and in what quantities. No items or locations are marked.

Sweep Points	Description
5	Cleaning tasks have been combined with dirt prevention methods. Tools, fixtures and gauges are free of residual magnetism.
4	Cleaning tasks and cleanliness inspection checklists have been combined.
3	The work area is cleaned daily but cleaning tasks and cleaning methods are not clearly defined.
2	The work area is cleaned, but not on a daily basis.
1	The work area has not been cleaned in a long time. Dirt and dust are evident everywhere.

5S Master Scoring

Schedule Points	Description
5	A periodic schedule/ methodology exists to maintain the first three steps of 5S at the highest possible levels for the entire facility.
4	The first three steps of 5S have become a habit in most of the facility or area.
3	Cleaning schedules are followed throughout the facility or area daily.
2	Cleaning schedules are followed in some areas.
1	No cleaning schedules or methodology exist, or existing schedules are not followed.
Sustain Points	**Description**
5	A disciplined system of control and maintenance is in place to assure that sorting, straightening, and sweeping are maintained at the highest possible level. Management is committed and responsible. 5S is part of every job.
4	5S practices and audits are in place throughout the facility. Improvements are identified and implemented. Management provides recognition and rewards in support of 5S.
3	5S audits are performed throughout the facility. Improvement areas are identified but not yet implemented. Management actively supports the 5S process.
2	5S training has occurred for all associates. 5S activity is apparent in some areas. 5S audits performed in some areas.
1	5S training has begun, but there is no other evidence of a 5S activity.

5S Score Sheet

5S Score	Improvement(s) Required to Achieve a Score of 5
Sort	
Straighten	
Sweep	
Schedule	
Sustain	

5S Total Score = _____

Score Divided By 5 = ___

Previous Score =

Scored By: _____

Location: _____

Date:

"Wow, you're serious about this stuff, aren't you?" exclaimed Jack.

"You haven't figured that out by now?" needled Christy.

"You better believe it, Jack," responded Mike. "It's serious business becoming a World Class company. Either we're all going to create an environment that relentlessly pursues World Class initiatives or we'll be corporate road kill. That's why I take this stuff very, very seriously."

"We get the point," said Josh.

"Good. Okay then, let's get going. We'll need the entire area put back together by lunch. Also, mark the floors with the colored tape and in a few weeks, if we don't think it'll change, we can paint the lines."

"How about the labeling? There's no way we'll finish everything this afternoon," said Joe.

"Do as much as you can for now. We'll have to stop everything by about one o'clock and organize the area. You'll finish the labeling over the next few weeks. Labeling always takes a long time and gets completed after the event. You can do it while the machine's running, a little bit each day. Okay, let's meet up here at the usual time for lunch. We'll go through a rehearsal for the report-out session right after we eat."

Everyone got up quickly and headed to the work center. Mike knew he didn't have to push them this morning; the two o'clock deadline was all that was needed. He was going to take some time to get organized for the report-out session so he could go through the presentation materials with the team at lunch.

CHAPTER 19
AT THE WORK CENTER

DAY 3 (9:00 A.M)

Mike went to the work area to help the teams as well as to answer last-minute questions.

"Hey, Mike," called out Harold. "We could use your help getting the racks from the paint booth. They promised they'd have them ready first thing in the morning, but some customer rush jobs had to get done. If we don't get them soon, we'll never be set up for later."

"I'll see what I can do." Mike headed off to the paint shop to see if he could coax the painters into completing the racks. Fortunately, when he got there, he saw the racks sitting in the corner. Evidently no one had a chance to bring the racks back to the work center, so he grabbed a pallet jack and wheeled them over. Getting anything painted during a three-day 5S event was always a challenge. Mike tried to discourage painting wherever possible but it never failed that the operators wanted to have their areas look good. Mike could never fault them for that.

"Mike, we're out of rolls of tape for the label machine. Can you find some more? We're not having any luck," pleaded Christy.

"I'll see what I could do." Fortunately, the local distributor was just down the road, and if need be, Mike would hop in his car to get Christy what she needed.

A little while later Mike heard his name again. "Over here, Mike," yelled Anthony while working on some electrical cables. "Look at these! The sheaths have some cuts and have to be replaced. Would've never known that without the 5S."

"Glad you found that. It's an accident waiting to happen," replied Mike.

"Check this out," called Jack by the set-up cart. "I've made foam cutouts for the tools. It's actually pretty neat. It's easy to find the exact place for everything and see what's missing. It's so obvious."

"Looks good."

"I could really use these techniques at home in my garage and basement," continued Jack

"It works anywhere," replied Mike. "I've done my garage and now there's no excuse for misplacing any of the yard tools. It really works. If my kids were younger I'd figure out how to use

5S techniques to keep their rooms clean."

"How old are your kids?"

"Eighteen and twenty. How about you, Jack, any kids?"

"Yeah, a seven-year-old girl."

"Then let me give you a suggestion. Clean your daughter's room and take a photo of it. Hang it up in the room and let her know what clean looks like. You'll thank me for that in a few years. Otherwise, it's a lost cause."

"Maybe I'll give it a try."

"If you do, let me know how it works. I used to always complain to my wife that the kids never did a good job cleaning their rooms and she used to always preach to me that they just didn't know what a good job was. Maybe some visual work instructions would've helped. I've always wondered about that."

"We're talking about kids here, Mike. Let's not get too carried away with Lean."

The morning went along smoothly albeit at a very fast pace. At this point, there was simply no time for any push back or infighting amongst the team. They were on a mission and Mike was always amazed how they helped each other on the last day. It was teamwork at its best.

CHAPTER 20
AT THE WORK CENTER

DAY 3 (11:30 A.M.)

"Get your lunches and I'll go over the re-port-out presentation while you're eating. If you want to leave for a smoke or whatever, go ahead." There was no time to lose, so Mike ignored Barb's earlier advice to avoid a working lunch. He hoped it wasn't a big mistake.

Brainstorming Ideas - Work Center 111 Team Captains - Joe Delaney & Josh Jenkins					
Improvement Activity	Category	Votes	Team Members	Status Complete	Other
1. Clean out all cabinets 4. Sort Items and Red Tag 6. Provide a place for cleaning supplies 7. Clean walls 32. Clean entire area 47. Organize file cabinet 48. Remove junk on top of machine	Cleaning	9	Fred Christy Mike Hubert	x x x x x x x	

2. Return tools to tool crib
13. Remove fixtures belonging to other work centers
19. Minimize trips to the tool crib
20. Set up tooling kanban
22. Need two tooling racks, one mounted on machine
24. Eliminate tool chests
29. Mark and label all tools
30. Group tooling by common use on top cabinet in
    holders
33. Minimize trips to tool crib
38. Re-evaluate all tools kept at machine and relocate
    to point of use
49. Add power tools
	Tooling	9	Josh
			Joe
			Harrold
			Paul
				x
				x
				x
				x
				x
				
				x
				
				x
				
				x
				x
					Ongoing
					Ongoing

3. Make set-up cart 23. Build set-up cart on wheels 37. Make set-up tools mobile	Set-up Cart	7	Jack Wendell	x x x	
5. Chips everywhere - clean up 26. Build chip guards 40. Cover pockets at base of machine 44. Provide retractable barrier to collect/redirect chips	Confine Chips	6	Anthony Randall	x x x	In process
8. Repaint machine a light color					Weekend
10. Mark staging areas 21. Standardize materail handling equipment 27. Identify finsihed goods in work center 31. Location of fixture pallets - color coded or numbered by machine	Material Handling	6		x x x x	
9. Make coolant collection trays 42. Make troughs for way lube	Control Fluids	6		x x	
12. Routings should reference tooling locations					TBD
14. Provide a hanger for mounting prints 15. Mount computer on column 16. Provide set-up visuals 17. Make bulletin board 41. Post set-up procedures 46. Provide a convenient holder for drawings 25. Provide fixture pictures on set-up sheets	Information	5		x x x x x x	 Ongoing
11. Mount retractable hose reel near point of use 45. Remove air line that is a tripping hazard		2		x x	
34. New ball screw for machine (it's in house) 18. Prepare TPM schedule 35. Get dedicated crane 36. Get new floor mat for operator 39. Provide a home for lifting straps and magnet 43. Make a shim box and organize 28. Eliminate clocking on and off jobs - it's waste		2 1 1 1 1		 x x x x	After Event Not Cost Justified

"Wow, we've really gotten a lot done," said Fred, somewhat surprised.

"The team's done well," concurred Mike. "Does anyone have any questions? Have I missed anything?"

"Yeah, we haven't talked about the crane at all, yet you put down it's not cost justified. Who made that decision?" asked Paul, defiantly.

"You're right, Paul, I might've jumped the gun on that one. The same issue came up at a set-up reduction event and I developed a cost benefit spreadsheet for the team to use. I'll go over it later if that's okay. But for now you'll have to take my word that it'll cost thousands of dollars to relocate the spare crane we have at the other end of the building, and it's just not worth it."

"So we're never going to do it?" pressed Paul.

"I didn't say that. We have the riggers in here occasionally when we relocate equipment. If we can get a really good deal to do it while they're here doing something else, we will. We'll need to calculate how much time it'll save on set-ups so we can determine a payback. If we can prove it to ourselves, Fred won't be a problem. That's why we keep these ideas in a hopper and wait until the opportunity presents itself."

Mike looked around the room. There were no more questions, so he moved onto the next topic. "I took a stab at an agenda for the report-out session." He walked over to the flip chart and walked the team through it.

Work Center 111

Report-Out Agenda

1. Introductions	3 Min.
2. Quick Review of 5S	3 Min.
3. Before 5S Pictures	3 Min.
4. 5S Tour	20 Min.
5. 5S Schedule	1 Min.
6. Just the Facts	2 Min.
7. Questions for the Team	5 Min.
8. Wrap-Up	3 Min.

"I'll take care of the first two items. Does anyone want to explain the 'before 5S' pictures? Remember, some of our guests will have no idea what the work area looked like before we cleaned and organized it." Mike scanned the room and was disappointed there were no volunteers. "How about you Joe? It's your work area so you know it best."

"I don't do public speaking."

"Okay, I'm not going to force anyone."

"I guess I can do it," said Paul, reluctantly.

"Great, thanks a lot. It'll have more credibility coming from you than me."

"That's easy to say, but I'm in charge of that work center and it's a little embarrassing to point out what a mess my area was."

"It's no different than any other area of the company. If anyone says anything negative, I'll ask them if we can take some pictures of their work areas or offices. But don't worry, it won't come to that."

"Mike, you don't need to say anything. I can easily talk about the mess of reports all over the accounting area. I'll help you out on this one, Paul," offered Fred

"Thanks a lot," replied Paul, astonished that Fred would help him. "Why would you do that?"

"Because I realize the accounting area's no different. It needs to be cleaned up and better organized. And it should be a lot easier for us to maintain our area than the challenge you guys have in the shop. Hell, we just have piles of paper all over that we have to deal with, not metal chips. It's gotta start somewhere in the office. I'll just need you guys to help out."

Wow, thought Mike, Fred just did more to bring the office and shop floor folks together than anything I could've done or said. I'm really glad he's on the team.

Mike continued orchestrating the report-out session. "Fred, get whatever data you can to update the 'Just the Facts' section. I want everyone to understand that Lean's about improving the business."

"Okay, but we don't have any data on set-up times yet."

"That'll have to wait until we have the machine up and running again, but you can fill in the section on square footage. I'll cover the last couple of items. Is everyone comfortable with the agenda?"

"Looks good," responded Christy and everyone else nodded in agreement. "But how about the tour; you didn't discuss that."

"I wanted to do that separately. Take a look at this. It's what we discussed this morning."

Tour	
1. Cleaning	Christy
2. Guards/Containment	Anthony
3. Racks & Tooling Kanban	Harold
4. Set-Up Cart	Wendell
5. Part Storage Locations	Josh

"How long do you want us to talk?" asked Christy.

"We have about twenty minutes for the tour so you can each take about four minutes. Make sure you point out everything you did because most of the people don't know the shop."

"Hell, they'd get lost if we left them alone out there," bellowed Anthony.

"You got that right," agreed Wendell.

"You've all busted your butts for three days, so you need to let them know what you did."

"How will we know when four minutes are up?" asked Anthony.

"When you have thirty seconds left, I'll raise my hand so you can start wrapping up. That'll keep us on schedule. And remember, you should make this part the highlight of the report-out session."

"If they're even interested," said Randall, ever the pessimist.

"They will be. Let's finish lunch and then I want to have a quick rehearsal with everyone who is presenting. Everyone else focus on cleaning up the work center and tying up the loose ends. We'll be down to help as soon as we're finished, but we don't have much time. Let's all meet back here at ten to two to clean up this room and get ready for the meeting."

After a very quick lunch, Mike met with the participants.

"Is everyone okay with the schedule and the order I put it in?"

"Fine with me," said Christy.

"Good. How about you, Wendell?"

"Yeah, what the hell, I'll be ready."

The other participants agreed as well. Mike then had everyone list the items they would point out and discuss on the tour. They all helped each other with their ideas and comments, and after about twenty-five minutes, they went out into the shop to help their teammates get ready.

CHAPTER 21

REPORT-OUT SESSION

DAY 3 (2:00 P.M.)

The Training Room quickly filled up. Mike had the team members sit on one side of the room and the guests on the other side. The seating arrangement made it easier to identify the team members as well as to facilitate the question and answer session at the end.

Mike checked his invite list to make sure everyone who indicated they would attend had arrived. This was a defining moment for the team and Mike always made sure to invite at least a dozen guests. And, of course, Peter's attendance was critical. When the last straggler walked in at five after two, Mike began. He introduced the team and had the guests introduce themselves. Mike was always amazed how a large group of people working at the same company for such a long time did not know who their teammates were. A 5S was a great ice breaker.

After Mike completed the introductions and

the three-minute 5S overview, Paul took the group through the "before 5S" pictures.

"Paul, did you really find a microwave oven in the cabinet or did Mike plant it?" asked a guest.

Paul's face turned red. "It was really there."

"So what were they cooking?" asked another jokingly.

"Nothing. It hasn't been used in years."

"Glad you found that," said Barb when Paul showed the picture of the frayed electrical cords. "That's a real safety problem."

"I can't believe there's so much junk in the Red Tag area," commented another.

Next Paul showed a picture of the work bench with tools piled haphazardly all over the place.

"Wow, it must take forever to find what you need," said another guest.

"It's not too bad," commented Wendell somewhat defensively. "I know where everything is." It was obvious the audience was not convinced, so Mike forwarded to another slide that none of the team members had seen.

"See this picture," said Mike, pointing to a picture of an office that had files all over the desk and floor, boxes in the corner and computer reports stacked on a chair. "This is the office of someone in this room. So before anyone gets any ideas about the plant, think about how well-organized we are in our offices. We waste a huge amount of time looking for stuff." Mike made his point. The team loved the slide. And the audience was whispering to each other, trying to figure out whose office it was.

Paul continued with his last picture. "Here's a couple of thousand dollars worth of carbide inserts we found at the work center and didn't even know were there. We found them in back of one of the drawers and returned them to the tool crib, so that'll save us some cash." That got everyone's attention.

Paul sat down and Mike took over. "That's it for the before pictures. Now we're going to the work center so the team can show you what they did. Please pick up a pair of safety glasses in the basket at the back of the room and then follow Christy to the work center.

Christy walked everyone around the area and explained everything they did.

"Why does the machine's paint job look like such a mess, Christy," asked a guest.

"We started sanding it so we can paint it this weekend."

"Why are you doing that?" asked another. "That sounds like a lot of work and expense."

Christy explained the concept of light colors and problem detection and the guests were taking it all in. You could see Christy's confidence growing and the pride she was taking in explaining how she cleaned a work center in a machine shop. Mike thought, this is what makes it all worthwhile.

Mike raised his hand and Christy started to wrap up. She looked at the agenda Mike had taped up in the work area and then passed the microphone to Anthony. Anthony explained in detail all of the guarding the team had built for the machine. Some of it was ingenious and the audience was visibly impressed. It was obvious Anthony could go on for fifteen minutes and Mike felt bad when he had to cut him off.

Next, Harold went through the tooling kanban.

"Why don't you want the operators to walk to the tool crib?" asked Peter.

Peter had been through a number of report-out sessions and could guess all the answers by now, but he wanted to accomplish two things: first, make sure the other guests appreciated the full benefits of a 5S, and second, let the team know he really was interested in what they had accomplished, which he genuinely was.

"Based on the data Mike showed us, we spend thousands of hours each year going to the tool crib and that is muda."

"Harold, why don't you explain what muda means to the group?" interjected Mike.

"Sure thing. Muda means waste and we don't want to spend our time walking back and forth all day. Besides, the tool crib's on the other side of the machine shop and we get tired going back and forth all day."

"So you're bringing the tool crib to the operators?" asked Peter.

"That's it. The tool crib attendant will be doing milk runs and fill this kanban with the tools I need based on the jobs in the box."

"Can you do this for just one work center?" asked another.

"Nope. That's why we'll be making tooling kanbans for all the work centers," responded Harold. "Any more questions?"

The tour continued with Wendell showing the set-up cart and Josh explaining how easy it would be to find parts with the new system. There was a lot of interest displayed by most of the guests. When Josh was finished, Mike led the group back up to the Training Room.

CHAPTER 22
REPORT-OUT SESSION
DAY 3 (2:40 P.M. RUNNING LATE)

After everyone was seated, Fred went through the "Just the Facts" slide. He explained that the accounting department would be the scorekeeper to verify improvements.

Just The Facts

Metric	Pre-5S	Post-5S
Set-up Times	56 Mins	
Set-ups/Annum	1,000	
Set-up Hours/Annum	933 Hours	
Square Feet	600 Sq. Ft.	400 Sq. Ft
Scrap per labor hour	$4.00	

"So, when do you fill in the last column?" asked a guest.

"We'll post results after sixty days. We want to complete the open items and let the operators get used to the new layout. We know set-up times will improve as a result of the new system for finding parts, plus all the other improvements that were made in the work center. We'll be filming set-ups in about two months and then we'll share the results with everyone.

"Thanks, Fred," said Mike, stepping in to wrap up. "Before we finish I just want to show you the list of everything we did as well as the remaining open items. The team's been very busy." Mike handed out the latest brainstorming list.

"When does the list get closed out?'" asked Barb.

"The team has sixty days to complete everything on the list as well as disposition everything in the Red Tag area. They've selected two captains who are responsible for keeping the process moving along and lining up resources, if necessary. Josh and Joe are the team captains."

"That concludes the presentation. Does anyone have any questions of the team?"

"I do. I noticed in the pictures that the team was wearing orange vests. How did you feel about that?" Barb asked, looking toward the team.

"Who would like to answer that?" asked Mike.

"I will," responded Josh eagerly. "When Mike explained that we'd have to wear the vests, I thought it was a bunch of bull. But after wearing it for three days, all I can say is you'll never know what it's like to wear the vest until you put it on yourself. I was proud to wear it."

Mike was taken aback by the answer. He never expected that from Josh. But he loved every minute of it. "Thanks, Josh. Anybody else with a question?"

"Yeah, I have one," said Randy. "It was hard enough giving Josh up for these three days and now you expect him to continue on as captain. You never mentioned that to me. He doesn't have the time, Mike."

"It won't take much time, Randy. The team will need to meet about one hour per week to organize and then the sub-teams will finish the open items a little at a time over the next two months."

"Mike, I respect what the team's accomplished, but you're asking the impossible."

Yeah right, thought Mike. He could care less what the team's done or the fact that Josh actually felt good about what he accomplished. Randy was single handedly tearing down the bridge Fred was building between manufacturing and the office.

"Mind if a say something, Mike?" asked Peter.

"Please go ahead."

"I've been traveling all over to visit our customers and I've been amazed by how they are not only practicing Lean techniques but demanding that we do it. If we're going to be a viable supplier, we have to become much more effective at everything. They expect us to become world class. I hear that time and again. So I want to make it clear to everyone that participating in Lean events is not an option, it's mandatory. In fact, I have asked Barb to modify our personnel review forms to include a section on Lean participation. No one will receive a promotion at this company unless he or she can demonstrate participation in a Lean improvement effort. That's all I have to say, Mike."

Wow, thought Mike. That'll finally shut Randy up. "Anybody else have a question?"

"I have another one," said Barb. "I'm interested in how the operators felt about it. After all, it is their work center."

"I'll answer that," volunteered Wendell. "I liked it because now we're finally going to get our new ball screw installed. Joe and I've been waiting a long time for that. It'll really help out."

"And how about you, Christy? What was it like for someone from the office?"

"It's hard work, Barb, I won't deny that. But I got to know a lot of people I would never have met. I also got a much better idea of the challenges the operators face every day. It was a good learning experience."

"And we appreciated her helping out," said Harold. "She really pulled her weight out there."

"Can I say something?" asked Anthony.

"Go ahead," responded Mike.

"I wasn't too keen on participating, especially after we got into the argument about the ball screw. But now I like the fact that we totally cleaned and inspected the machine and it'll make my job a lot easier. That machine's had a lot of downtime and I'm sure it'll be a lot better now."

"So, it's a lot more than just cleaning the work area?" asked another guest.

"Let me answer that, Mike," said Hubert, recalling his questioning the same thing at the outset of the event. "I really didn't want any part of this because I didn't want to spend so much time cleaning an area that would only get dirty again. But now I know it's so much more than cleaning. We'll be able to do our jobs a lot better now."

"Thanks, Hubert." Mike scanned the room. "If there are no more questions I'd like Peter to come up to the front of the room to help me rec-

207

ognize the team."

Peter joined Mike at the front of the room and, one by one, they called each team member up to receive a Lean Team T-shirt and certificate of recognition. Then the entire team had its picture taken to post on the Lean bulletin board.

Mike concluded the meeting asking everyone to give the team a round of applause for the great job they had done. The guests left and Mike asked the team to stay for a few more minutes to wrap things up.

"We're never going to get away from you," joked Wendell.

"I just have a couple of things. Before leaving, I'd like the team captains to schedule a team meeting within the next week so that you keep the momentum going. At that meeting, you should come up with a schedule for completing the open items as well as a work plan. I'll send the captains a copy of all the charts and notes tomorrow. I'll also have the 5S audit team score the area in a few weeks. Finally, I'd like to personally thank all of you for a job well done. This has been one of the best events I've been part of. Now if you all can just 5S this room, you can be rid of me."

Mike started to 5S his area and gather up his materials when Fred walked over.

"You look a little tired."

"I'm exhausted at the end of these events."

"I don't know how you keep up the pace."

"What choice do we have if we want to stay in business? And it's worth it to hear that the team members, for the most part, got something out of it. So, how about you? What did you think, Fred?"

"It was quite an experience, I'll admit that. I learned a lot."

"Would you do it again?"

"I would."

"How about leading an event? We could really use them in the office."

"I said I would and I wasn't kidding. I'll need your help on the first one, though."

"Great, let's double team an office 5S and then you'll be ready to do it by yourself."

"One thing's bothering me, though."

"What's that?"

"Randy. He's really dug his heels in and Peter basically told him he's gotta change."

"Peter's right. At some point, Randy has to realize that he's gotta hop on board this train or it's leaving without him. He's in a leadership position and it's crucial he supports the effort and participates. Also, he can't make his subordinates feel guilty for participating."

"I know, but it's just going to be so hard for him."

"It's going to be a lot harder for the rest of us if he doesn't get on board. We can't let him bring us all down."

"Aren't you being a little hard on him?"

"Hell no. Take Randall for example..."

"I was going to ask you about him."

"Randall doesn't get it. He's a concrete head, or at least he is now. He may or may not ever get it. But which concrete head can do more damage, Randall or Randy?"

"It's no contest."

"You're right. Randall can go back to his job and keep doing it the old way without dire consequences, at least for the time being. But Randy can be a huge roadblock to this entire organization. Leadership must get on board or be moved aside. It's as simple as that, Fred."

"That's what I was afraid you'd say."

"Because you know it's right. So see what you can do to convince him to give it a chance. If he doesn't, your friend will be in big trouble."

"I've been trying, believe me."

"I know. You just have to keep at it."

Mike picked up his material and headed back to his office. He reflected on the event. Another one down, hundreds more to go. But he knew it was worth it. These events would lead to greater job security for his fellow employees, improved customer service and market position for the company, and he hoped, in some small way would improve the country's manufacturing prowess.

Chapter 23
Lunch Meeting

Two Weeks After Event

"So, Randy," said Fred as he poured sugar into his cup of Chinese tea, "Have you spent any quality time with Josh, talking about the event?"

"Yeah, I went to lunch with Josh the other day. I owed it to you to see what he really thought about the event."

"That's crap. You don't owe me anything; you owe it to yourself and the company."

"C'mon, cut me some slack. At least I'm trying to understand this stuff."

"So what did Josh have to say?"

"He said it was hard work but he actually enjoyed the event."

"Good, what else?"

"He explained how the team didn't just clean the machine, but also set the foundation to significantly reduce set-up times."

"And. . ."

"Well, I never thought much about the importance of set-up time, so he went into a lengthy discussion about its impact on deliveries, inventory, and quality. I'm starting to see how one thing can lead to another and ultimately lead to improvements in the fundamentals of the business."

"That's great," said Fred, grinning from ear to ear. "This Lean stuff is all about the cumulative impact of thousands and thousands of small improvements happening every day for years to come. Did Josh tell you exactly how much the set-ups have been improved?"

"Yeah, he told me they're down by forty-two percent! It's crazy how cleaning up a work center would yield such results."

"Not really, once you see how poorly things are organized. Heck, Josh saved twelve minutes per part with his new method for sorting the material by the last digit of the part number. We can all help each other get a lot better. That's what so neat about this stuff."

"But, I still don't understand where we're going to get the people or time to do all of this?"

"That's where you come in, Randy. You have

to make the time. We've been doing that in accounting, IT, and purchasing for the last year. It's not easy, but what's the alternative? The status quo isn't good enough anymore."

"No way I can spare anyone else, Fred. We're already behind on every development project we're working on."

"That's precisely why you need to learn Lean. And I'm not saying you have to spend time on 5Ss in the shop. You need to use Lean tools in your area so you can become more efficient."

"Now what are you talking about?"

"Mike conducted a Value Stream Mapping event in accounting a few months ago and we eliminated about fifty percent of the time it takes to process payables. It was a real eye opener for all of us."

"What the heck's Value Stream Mapping? Another one of Mike's buzz words?"

"I'll show you what we did when we get back to the office. The point is, that you can apply these Lean tools anywhere. And if you do it correctly, you'll free up a lot of time. Then you can devote that time to continuous improvement. But you have to start somewhere, Randy. I'm telling you this stuff works, but you have to give it a chance."

"Sounds too good to be true."

"It's no use *telling* you about this. Unless you experience it for yourself, you'll never believe me. You have to jump right in."

"Let me think about it."

"That's the same as saying no, so don't BS me."

"So how do I get you off my back?"

"Participate in an event in your area as soon as possible, that's how."

"With everything I have on my plate..."

"Enough with the excuses, Randy. We've worked together a long time. Trust me; this Lean stuff isn't going away. It's time for action."

"Would you help with an event?"

"Sure will. And please, support Josh in his efforts to finish up the 5S at Work Center 111."

"Okay already, I give in, I'll do it. Let's eat lunch already—I'm starved."

INDEX